WATCH THE WIND

McGRAW-HILL READING

WATCH THE WIND

Authors

Elizabeth Sulzby
   The University of Michigan

James Hoffman
   University of Texas at Austin

Jerome Niles
   Virginia Polytechnic Institute

Timothy Shanahan
   University of Illinois at Chicago

William H. Teale
   University of Texas at San Antonio

Literature Consultant

Sylvia Peña
   University of Houston

Contributing Authors

John Anthony Angelo
   Salinas High School,
   California

Lillian K. Boyd
   Detroit Public Schools

Kay M. Kincade
   Central State University,
   Edmond, Oklahoma

Jacqueline Kiraithe de Córdova
   California State University
   at Fullerton

Leon Lessinger, CEO
   Health Champions, Inc.
   Beverly Hills, California

Charles Mangrum II
   University of Miami,
   Coral Gables, Florida

George Mason
   University of Georgia

Kathleen Naylor
   Educational Consultant
   Brea, California

Karen S. Urbschat
   Wayne County Intermediate
   School District, Michigan

Arnold Webb
   Research For Better Schools
   Philadelphia, Pennsylvania

McGraw-Hill School Division

New York   Oklahoma City   St. Louis   San Francisco   Dallas   Atlanta

The title of this book, "Watch The Wind," is taken from the poem "Afternoon on a Hill" by Edna St. Vincent Millay.

Cover Illustration: Roy Pendleton

Grateful acknowledgment for permission to reprint copyrighted material, illustrations and photographs appearing in this book is made on pages 284 and 285 of this book, which is hereby made a part of this copyright page.

ISBN 0-07-042080-7

McGraw-Hill School Division
1200 Northwest 63rd Street
Oklahoma City, Oklahoma 73116-5712

2 3 4 5 6 7 8 9 0—8 9 7 6 5 4 3 2 1 0

Contents

Reading on Your Own ◆ 10

Part One ◆ People ◆ 12

Part Two ◆ Places ◆ 74

Part Three ◆ Great Creatures ◆ 140

Part Four ◆ Small Creatures ◆ 202

Part One

People

Part Opener	12
Vocabulary Builder:	14
Using Words About People	
Theme Setter:	16
◇ **Max** by Rachel Isadora	
Comprehension Builder:	19
Understanding What Is Real and	
Not Real in Stories	
No Time for Tina by Bonnie Knight	20
◇ **Worthington Botts and the Steam**	
Machine by Betty Baker	26
◇ **Picture People,** a poem	36
by Myra Cohn Livingston	
Strategy Builder:	37
Understanding Stories That Seem Real	
Jenny and the Tennis Nut	38
by Janet Schulman	
◇ **Watch Out, Ronald Morgan!**	46
by Patricia Reilly Giff	
Readers' Choice:	56
◇ **I Have a Sister—My Sister Is Deaf**	
by Jeanne Whitehouse Peterson	
About the Author:	68
Jeanne Whitehouse Peterson	
More Books About People	69
Making All the Connections: Speaking	70
and Listening•Doing an Interview	

◇ Award-winning
book or author

Part Two

Places

Part Opener   74

Vocabulary Builder: 76
    Using Words About Places

Theme Setter: 78
In My Treehouse by Alice Schertle

Comprehension Builder: 81
    Understanding Order in a Story

◇ **The Boy Who Saved Holland**   82
    by Mary Mapes Dodge

◇ **The Best New Thing** by Isaac Asimov   90

Watching the Stars, a how-to story   100

◇ **Afternoon on a Hill,** a poem   102
    by Edna St. Vincent Millay

Strategy Builder: 103
    Understanding Stories that Give Facts

Transportation by Martin Oshiro   104

The Newest Cities of All   110
    by Judy Rosenbaum

Readers' Choice: 118

◇ **Evan's Corner** by Elizabeth Starr Hill

About the Author: Elizabeth Starr Hill   132

More Books About Places   133

Making All the Connections: Speaking   134
    and Listening•Reading Something
    New•Thinking About Places•Writing
    About a Special Place

Part Three   Great Creatures

Part Opener   140

Vocabulary Builder: 142
    Using Words About Great Creatures

Theme Setter: 144
◇ **Little Gorilla** by Ruth Bornstein

Comprehension Builder: 147
    Understanding the Big Idea

◇ **What Is That Alligator Saying?**   148
    by Ruth Belov Gross

◇ **Digging Up Dinosaurs** by Aliki   156

◇ **The Whales Off Wales,** a poem   166
    by X.J. Kennedy

Strategy Builder: 167
    Understanding Fables

◇ **Aesop's Fables**   168
    The Lion and the Mouse
    The Greedy Dog

◇ **Belling the Cat,** a play   174
    by Laura Schenone,
    based on the fable by Aesop

Readers' Choice: 184
◇ **Veronica** by Roger Duvoisin

About the Author: Roger Duvoisin   196

More Books About Great Creatures   197

Making All the Connections: Speaking   198
    and Listening•Thinking
    About Pictures

◇ Award-winning
book or author

8

Part Four

Small Creatures

Part Opener   202
Vocabulary Builder: 204
    Using Words About Small Creatures
Theme Setter: 206
◇ **Horton Hears a Who!** by Dr. Seuss
Comprehension Builder: Understanding
    How to Compare Things   209
◇ **The Rice Bowl Pet** by Patricia Miles Martin   210
◇ **Janey's Boss** by Lilian Moore   216
A Stop Sign for Birds, a how-to story   224
Strategy Builder: Understanding Poems   225
◇ **Bug Poems:** *I Like Bugs* by Margaret Wise   226
Brown, *Little Talk* by Aileen Fisher
◇ **Cat and Mouse Poems:** *Cats* by Eleanor   230
    Farjeon; *Cat* by Mary Britton Miller;
    Mice by Rose Fyleman;
    The Old Woman by Beatrix Potter
◇ Readers' Choice: **Alexander and the**   238
    Wind-up Mouse by Leo Lionni
About the Author: Leo Lionni   254
More Books About Small Creatures   255
Making All the Connections: Speaking   256
    and Listening•Reading Something New•
    Thinking About Small Creatures•Writing
    How-to Directions
Writer's Handbook   262
Glossary   268

Reading on Your Own

I like to read. Reading is fun. I know some ways to help you read better.

Before You Read

- ◆ Read the name of the story.
- ◆ Look at the pictures.
- ◆ Think about what you will read.

As You Read

- ◆ Stop after each page.
- ◆ Think about what you have read.
- ◆ Think about what might come next.

Sometimes you see a word you don't know. Try these steps.

1. Try to say the word.

2. Read the words before and after the word.

3. Look up the word in the glossary at the back of the book.

4. Ask for help.

After You Read

◆ Tell the story in your own words.

PART ONE

People

Everybody says
I look just like my mother.
Everybody says
I'm the image of Aunt Bee.
Everybody says
My nose is like my father's
But *I* want to look like *ME*!

Everybody Says
by Dorothy Aldis

◆

People, people everywhere—and they are all different. In these stories you will find out about many people. As you read, think: Will you find out something new about yourself?

Using Words About People

Starting with What You Know

Think about people. What ideas can you come up with? The words in the box tell about people. Use these words and other words you know to answer the questions after the box.

tall	happy	pretty
think	small	work
funny	learn	laugh

Words can be fun.

What are some ways people look? What things do people do? What ways do people act?

Building a Word Map

The word map shows how some of the words in the box above go together. Think about words you can put on the map.

What People Do
think
learn

PEOPLE

What People Look Like
tall
pretty

Finishing a Story

Look at the following story about a girl named Lucy. Some words are left out. Think of the words you would use to finish the story. Use the words from the box and word map in this lesson for ideas. Complete the story.

Lucy was writing a letter to her new pen pal, Tim. They had never met. Lucy wanted to tell Tim what she was like.

"I am very _____," wrote Lucy. "I have _____ hair. My feet are _____. I like to _____ in the playground. I also like to _____. My friends say I am a very _____ girl."

Share your story with your class. What words did the children in your class use? How were the stories different?

As You Read

In this part of the book, you will read about people and things they do. Keep a Reader's Log. A Reader's Log will help you remember thoughts, ideas, and new words. Start the log with the word map. Write new words on your map as you find them.

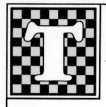

Max is a great baseball player. On his way to the game one day, he finds out that he is great at another thing, too.

MAX

◆

by Rachel Isadora

Max is a great baseball player. He can jump, run fast, and hit many home runs. Every Saturday he plays with his team in the park.

On Saturday mornings he walks with his sister Lisa to her dancing school. The school is on the way to the park.

One Saturday when they reach the school, Max still has lots of time before the game is to start. Lisa asks him if he wants to come to her dance class.

Max doesn't really want to, but he says all right. Soon the class starts.

Max is invited to join the class, but he must take off his baseball shoes first. He stretches at the bar. He does the jump. He is having fun.

Just as the class lines up to do leaps, Lisa points to the clock. It is time for Max to leave.

Max doesn't want to leave before he leaps. He stretches again, then takes his turn. Then he must go.

He leaps all the way to the park. He is late. Everybody is waiting for him. He goes up to bat.

He swings.

A home run!

Now Max has a new way to warm up for the game on Saturdays. He goes to dancing class.

Thinking About the Theme

1. How is Max different from most other baseball players?

2. Max tried a new thing. What other things do you think he might like to try? Would you like to try these things too?

Understanding What Is Real and Not Real in Stories

for **No Time for Tina** and **Worthington Botts and the Steam Machine**

Which could really happen?

Thinking About What Is Real and Not Real in Stories

Some things that happen in stories could really happen. Some things could not really happen. Things that could not happen are called **fantasy.** Read this story. Which part seems real? Which part seems like fantasy?

> Todd walks his dog. When they come back, the dog says, "Thanks, Todd."

As You Read

As you read the two stories that follow, ask yourself this question. "What is real and what is fantasy?" Use the notes in blue to help you.

19

Tina is tired of having to do the right thing at the right time. She wishes that she could always play and have fun. How will she feel when her wish seems to come true?

No Time for Tina

by Bonnie Knight

This part seems real.

"It is time for bed," Tina's mother said to Tina.

"Already? It's always time to do something," Tina said. "I wish there was no time. Then I could always have fun."

Tina went to sleep.

This is fantasy.

All at once, Tina's bed seemed to turn round and round.

"Stop!" said Tina. The bed stopped.

Tina looked for her clock, but her clock was not there.

"That is funny," said Tina. She got out of bed and ran outside into the yard. Everything and everyone was green. The sun and the moon were in the sky, and they were also green. Tina couldn't tell if it was daytime or nighttime.

A green sun is not real.

Tina went around the corner of her house and saw a little green man high up in a tree.

"Is it nighttime or daytime?" Tina asked.

"It is no time at all," answered the little green man. "This is the town of No Time. I am Mr. Wish and I have invited you to our town."

Tina was happy, because now she could always play.

Tina and Mr. Wish went down the road and stopped at the corner.

"Why does everyone run?" Tina asked.

"Everyone must run. People have no time to rest in this town," said Mr. Wish.

"Do the children go to school?" asked Tina.

"No, because it is never time to go to school," answered Mr. Wish. "And now *we* must also run. There is no time to rest either."

They turned the corner and ran all around the town.

A bat flew by, because there was no daytime. A cat ran after a mouse, because there was no nighttime.

"I want to rest," Tina said.

"There is no time to rest," said Mr. Wish.

Tina wished there was time to rest and time to go to school.

Tina sat down on the green grass.

"There is no time to sit, either," said Mr. Wish. "Get up, Tina. Get up."

"I don't want to get up," said Tina.

"But it is already time to wake up," said Tina's mother.

Tina looked around. Mr. Wish was not there, but Mother was there by the bed.

"It wasn't real. It was just a scary dream!" Tina said.

The end seems real.

Tina looked at her clock. She was happy to have time again.

A Reader Says

Tina's dream was a little scary. I think she was glad to wake up and be in the real world again.

How did you feel about the story?

After You Read

Thinking About What You Read

1. Why did Tina think she would have more fun if there were more time?

2. How was Mr. Wish different from Tina and her mother?

3. Why did Tina wish there was time to rest in the town of No Time?

4. How did her dream make Tina happy to have time again?

Thinking About How You Read

How did knowing that some things could really happen and some things were fantasy help you understand this story?

Sharing and Listening

Find a part of Tina's dream that you liked or didn't like. Tell why you did or did not like it. Listen as other people tell what they liked or didn't like about the dream.

Writing

Write a story about the people who lived in No Time. What would things be like for people who live there?

105339

In this story, you will meet a boy who loves to read. But he gets a big surprise when he makes a machine to help him have more time for reading.

Worthington Botts and the Steam Machine

by Betty Baker

Worthington Botts always said, "If someone wrote it, I can know it." And Worthington wanted to know everything.

His friends said he already did know a lot. He already did know how to make a house of logs and how to fix a clock. He could also play baseball.

But whatever he did, he tried to read at the same time.

"Worthington Botts," his friends yelled, "stop reading those cans! You have to watch for the ball."

"The ball never comes this far," said Worthington.

"It will," said his friends.

"It will when we play the Tufftown Nine. You have to watch!"

But Worthington Botts went on reading. He read when he ate, when he milked the cow and when he weeded his mother's garden.

"Worthington Botts," his mother yelled, "stop reading that book and look what you are doing!"

"I can't stop reading," Worthington answered. "There are too many things I don't know."

Then one day Worthington read about a steam machine. It looked like a man and walked like one. It could pull carts and clean floors. The book showed how it worked.

"I could make that," said Worthington Botts. Then he said, "I will! My steam machine will pull carts and pull weeds and milk the cow and lead me down the side of the road. Then no one will yell when I try to read."

His friends said, "Will it play baseball?"

"Why not?" said Worthington Botts.

"Then we can beat the Tufftown Nine!" said his friends.

And they stopped playing baseball and helped to find pipes and wheels and cans and other things Worthington Botts needed to make the steam machine.

The steam machine was very big and had a funny hat on its head. Worthington Botts started the machine and waited.

His friends said, "When will it walk?"

"When steam comes out of its pipe," said Worthington Botts.

"There it comes!" they yelled.

Worthington got up. He pulled this and turned that. The steam machine started to walk.

The steam machine walked to the garden. It creaked and went *clang*, *bang*. The steam machine pulled the weeds and also the grass and went on into the flowers.

"Worthington Botts," his mother yelled, "get that thing out of my garden!"

Worthington had to fix the garden. He could not read at all that day. "But I will tomorrow," he said, "when the steam machine milks the cow."

But the cow didn't like the clang and the creak. She mooed and kicked the steam machine, and Worthington had to fix its legs.

He could not read that day, either. "But I will tomorrow," he said, "when I go to play baseball with the Tufftown Nine."

He tied one end of a rope around himself. He tied the other end to the steam machine so it could lead him out of the yard and down the side of the road. The road turned. The steam machine did not. It went on with a *clang*, a *bang*, and a cloud of steam.

Worthington Botts had to go with it. He fell and got bumped and was chased by bees before he got away from the steam machine. His leg hurt and his book was lost. But he got to the road and went on to the game.

His friends yelled, "Where is the steam machine? We will lose the game without it. You have to get it right away!" said his friends.

But it was too late. There was a clang and a bang. Down the road came the Tufftown Nine and the steam machine.

"What will we do?" said his friends.

"Play ball!" the umpire said.

"Don't be afraid," Worthington said. "That steam machine hasn't worked yet. And I will watch for the ball. I promise!"

Worthington saw something to read on the fence, but he didn't try to read it. Cans rolled by, but he didn't try to read them.

The Tufftown Nine had three men on.

The steam machine clanged up to bat.

A newspaper fell nearby. Worthington started to read the newspaper.

"Worthington Botts! The ball!"

Worthington looked up from the newspaper just in time.

"Out!" said the umpire.

But the machine had started to run. Soon the Tufftown Nine were running, too. "Help!" they yelled.

"I'll stop it with the ball," Worthington said.

The ball hit the machine's leg. The machine ran faster and faster. Then it fell over in a cloud of steam.

"Play ball!" said the umpire.

But the Tufftown Nine had run away.

"You win," the umpire said.

Worthington's friends started to yell. "Your steam machine worked just great!" they said. "Can you make it play some other game?"

"Yes, but I will not," said Worthington Botts. "I am not going to fix it again."

He took it home and put it down next to him while he milked the cow. Without the legs it was just right to hold a book.

A Reader Says

I like to read too, but I think that Worthington read too much.

How did you feel about the story?

After You Read

Thinking About What You Read

1. In what way was reading bad for Worthington?

2. Why didn't he have much time to read after he made the machine?

3. If the steam machine had played on Worthington's side, how would the story be different?

4. Why didn't he fix his machine?

Thinking About How You Read

How did knowing that some things could really happen and some things were fantasy help you understand the story?

Sharing and Listening

Worthington wanted his machine to work for him. Tell if you think the machine worked for him or did not work for him. Why? Then listen as other people tell their ideas.

Writing

Write some of the things that a real boy like Worthington could do that the steam machine could not do.

PICTURE PEOPLE

I like to peek
  inside a book
  where all the picture people look.

I like to peek
  at them and see
  if they are peeking back at me.

Myra Cohn Livingston

36

Understanding Stories That Seem Real

for **Jenny and the Tennis Nut** and **Watch Out, Ronald Morgan**

Starting with What You Know

Some stories that you have read seem as if they could have really happened. What stories like this have you read?

Thinking About Stories That Seem Real

Stories that are made up but seem real are called **realistic** stories. The people and the animals in these stories seem real. The things they do seem real. The places in the story seem real.

As You Read

As you read the two stories that follow, ask yourself this question. "What things do the people say or do that make the story seem realistic?" Use the notes in blue to help you.

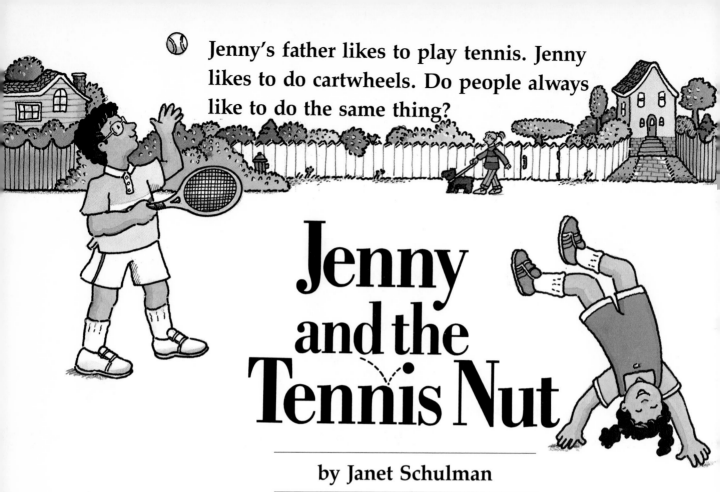

Jenny's father likes to play tennis. Jenny likes to do cartwheels. Do people always like to do the same thing?

Jenny and the Tennis Nut

by Janet Schulman

Jenny and her father are the people in the story.

Jenny was standing on her hands. "Fifty, fifty-one, fifty-two," she counted. Just then her father came into the room.

"Look at me, Dad. It's my best handstand yet," she said.

"What's so great about it?" asked her father.

She looked at him and said, "I have been standing like this for a long time."

"Well, I have been standing like this much longer. For years, in fact," said her father.

"Get right side up now. I have a surprise
for you." He gave her a funny-looking box.

"It looks like a tennis racket and it feels
like a tennis racket," said Jenny. She opened
the box. "It is a tennis racket."

"Well, what do you say?" asked her father.

"I don't know how to play tennis," said
Jenny.

"I am going to teach you, and this will be
your racket," he said.

"What if I don't like tennis?" she asked.

"Oh, Jenny," answered her father. "You
are going to love tennis. I love tennis. Your
mother loves tennis. And you will love
tennis, too."

Jenny and her
father talk and
do things like real
people.

Think about how
Jenny feels.

39

But Jenny did not hear him. She stood the racket up on her nose. "Look, I'm a seal playing tennis," she said.

Crash! The racket fell. "It is not a plaything," said her father.

"But, Daddy, did you see what I did?" Jenny asked. "I bet I could get real good at being a tennis-playing seal."

Her father grinned. "I bet you could get real good at being a tennis-playing girl."

He picked up his racket and some tennis balls. "Come on outside, Jenny. Let us play for a while. We can hit the ball on the side of the house," he said.

He made a line on the side of the house.

"Pretend that this line is the net," he said. "Hit the ball like this."

Thonk went the ball. He stretched and hit the ball again and again.

Thonk, hit. *Thonk*, hit. *Thonk*, hit.

He huffed and he puffed. But he did not care. He loved hitting a tennis ball. He loved it so much that he forgot about teaching Jenny.

Think about what is happening. Jenny and her father like to do different things.

Think about what Jenny's father wants to happen.

Think about where things are happening. The house seems real.

41

At last he stopped. "Now you try," he said. He threw a ball to her. She swung. *Swish* went her racket. "Keep your eye on the ball and you won't miss," he said.

He threw another ball to her. She watched the ball. She hit it. *Zing* went the ball over the fence and into Mrs. Wister's yard.

"I'll get the ball," said Jenny. She took a running start and jumped up, up and over Mrs. Wister's fence.

"That was pretty good," said her father. Jenny smiled.

"Oh, I can jump a lot better than that," she said.

"I was talking about how you hit the ball," he said. "But stand with your side to the net. That is the right way to stand when you hit the ball."

Jenny made a face. "There are too many things to think about in tennis," she said.

"Don't give up. It will get easier," he said. He threw a ball to her.

She did not take her eye off the ball. She stood with her side to the net. She swung the racket. *Thonk* went the ball.

"That's great!" said her father. "You will be a winner in no time."

"Oh, Daddy, stop it," she said.

"Don't you want to be a great tennis player?" he asked.

"No. I want to be a great circus acrobat," she said.

"A circus acrobat! There are not many circuses looking for acrobats nowadays. But there are lots of places for tennis players to play," he said.

"You only think about one thing. Tennis, tennis, tennis. Oh, Dad," she said. "You are a tennis nut. I already have something I can do well. Look!"

She ran to the grass. She did four cartwheels and three flips.

Think about what
Jenny is saying.
This is important.

43

Her dad smiled.

"I'm going to get you a bar so that you can work on being an acrobat."

Jenny threw her arms around him. "It's all right to do my tricks?" she asked.

"Yes. It is. I want you to. Being an acrobat is right for you," he said.

They were both happy. Jenny looked up at her father. "There is something else, Dad. If you ever want another game, I'll always be ready to teach you cartwheels and flips. You would love it."

And she grinned at him upside down.

Think about the ending. It seems like something that could happen in real life.

A Reader Says

Jenny should have tried harder. She might have turned out to be a tennis star.

How did you feel about the story?

After You Read

Thinking About What You Read

1. Why didn't Jenny like tennis?

2. Do you think Jenny could have been a good tennis player? Why?

3. How did Jenny's dad find out at last that being an acrobat was right for Jenny?

4. How did Jenny feel about her dad at the end of the story?

Thinking About How You Read

What did Jenny and her father say or do that made the story seem real?

Sharing and Listening

Think of Jenny and her dad. Then tell why people like to do different things. Tell what games you like. Listen as other people give their ideas and tell what games they like.

Writing

Pretend that you are Jenny. Write a note to a friend telling how you came to be an acrobat.

Glasses can help some people see better.
Can new glasses make Ronald the
"superkid" of the school?

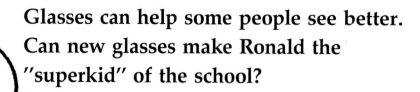

Watch OUT, Ronald Morgan!

by Patricia Reilly Giff

It all started when the bell rang.

I raced across the school yard and slid on some ice.

"Watch out!" Rosemary yelled.

But it was too late. I bumped into her and she landed in the snow.

After I took off my jacket, I fed the fish. I fed Frank, the gerbil, too.

"Oh, no," Rosemary said. "You fed the gerbil food to Goldie."

"Oh," I said. "The boxes look the same."

Billy frowned. "Can't you read? F is for fish. G is for gerbil."

"Don't worry," said Michael, my best friend. He put more water into the fish bowl.

Then it was time for book reports. "Who would like to be first to read a report?" Miss Tyler asked.

I ducked behind my desk.

"Ronald Morgan," said Miss Tyler.

"My book is *Lennie Lion*," I said. I held up my report to see the words. "This book is about a lion named Lennie. He's scary and good."

"Great," said Jan.

"Grr," said Michael.

"Very good," said Miss Tyler.

Later that day we looked out the window. Snow was everywhere. "It's time for a winter classroom," said Miss Tyler.

I sat at my desk and drew a snowflake. Then I cut it out.

Tom said, "Ronald Morgan, that's a funny snowflake. Why don't you cut on the lines?"

And Rosemary said, "I think your snowflake is melting."

When it was time to go home, Miss Tyler gave me a note for my mother and father. "Maybe you need glasses," she said.

At break the next day, Marc asked, "When do you get your glasses?"

I ate some nuts. "I go today."

Michael asked, "Can I go with you?"

After school, I went with Michael to get my glasses. We passed my father's tie store on the way. I waved to him and he waved back. In Doctor Sims's window was a giant pair of glasses. Michael and I pretended they were a monster's glasses.

"Look at this E," said Doctor Sims. "Which way does it point?"

I tried to see it. The E looked smaller and smaller.

Then Doctor Sims said, "It's hard for you to see it. Glasses will help. They will make everything look sharp and clear."

Next I tried on a pair of red frames. They slid down over my nose. Then I put on blue frames.

"Good," said my mother and Michael.

"Just wait till tomorrow," I said. "I'll be the best ballplayer, the best reader, the best everything. I'll be the superkid of the school."

Before school, I threw some snowballs.

"You missed!" Jimmy yelled, and threw one at me. It landed right on my nose. I felt it melting on my face.

Michael started to worry. "How come your glasses don't work?"

In the classroom, I took off my jacket.

"Who is going to feed the fish?" asked Miss Tyler.

I ran to give Goldie some food. This time I looked at the box. "G is for Goldie," I said. "F is for Frank."

"Oh, no," said Billy. "F is for fish. G is for gerbil."

And Michael frowned. "I don't think your glasses help."

At lunch break I put my glasses in my jacket. Alice looked at me. "Where are your blue glasses?" she whispered. "You forgot to put them on."

I frowned. "I have bad glasses. I'll never be the superkid of the class."

When the school bell rang to go home, Miss Tyler gave me another note.

My mother helped me with some of the words.

Dear Ronald,
I know you are sad about your glasses. But glasses will not make you a great thrower. And you'll still trip if you don't watch out.
Glasses will help you. They make everything clear. Please wear your glasses tomorrow. We will make snowmen for our winter classroom.
Love,
Miss Tyler
P.S. Don't worry. You ARE a superkid.

The next day in school I drew a snowman. I held it up to cut it out. "You know what?" I said. "Miss Tyler is right. The lines are sharp and clear."

"Good snowman!" Rosemary cheered.

And Miss Tyler said, "Just what we need for our winter classroom."

I drew a few more lines. "Now he's a superkid snowman," I said.

We all cheered.

A Reader Says

Ronald Morgan doesn't have to worry. When he gets used to glasses, he will do better.

How did you feel about the story?

After You Read

Thinking About What You Read

1. How did Miss Tyler know Ronald needed glasses?

2. How did the other children in the class feel about Ronald before he got his glasses? After he got his glasses?

3. Why did Ronald take off his glasses during school?

4. Why did Ronald think glasses would turn him into a superkid?

Thinking About How You Read

What feelings did Ronald have that made him seem like a real person?

Sharing and Listening

Tell which of the people you liked in the story. Why? Then listen as others tell which people they liked in the story.

Writing

Write some of the ways glasses can help people who need them. Then write some things that are not different after you get glasses.

READERS' CHOICE

How would you tell about someone you know very well? In this story, a girl tells about her sister and the things they do together.

I Have a Sister
My Sister Is Deaf

by Jeanne Whitehouse Peterson

I have a sister. My sister is deaf. She is special. There are not many sisters like mine.

My sister can play the piano. She likes to feel the deep rumbling chords. But she will never be able to sing. She cannot hear the tune.

My sister can dance with a partner or march in a line. She likes to leap, to tumble, to roll, to climb to the top of the monkey bars.

56

She watches me as we climb. I watch her, too. She cannot hear me shout, "Look out!" But she can see me swinging her way. She laughs and swings backward, trying to catch my legs.

I have a sister who likes to go with me out to the grassy lot behind our house. Today we are stalking deer. I turn to speak to her. I use no voice, just my fingers and my lips. She understands, and walks behind me, stepping where I step.

I am the one who listens for small sounds. She is the one who watches for quick movements in the grass.

When my sister was very small, when I went to school and she did not, my sister learned to say some words. Each day she sat on the floor with our mother, playing with some toys we keep in an old shoe box. "It's a ball," our mother would say. "It's a dog. It's a book."

When I came home, I also sat on the floor. My sister put her hands into the box. She smiled and said, "Ball."

Baaaa! it sounded to me. "It's a ball," I repeated, just like our mother did.

My sister nodded and smiled. "Ball," she said once more. Again it sounded like *baaaa!* to me.

Now my sister has started going to my school, although our mother still helps her speak and lip-read at home. The teacher and children do not understand every word she says, like *sister* or *water* or *thumb*. Today the children in her room told me, "Your sister said *blue!*"

Well, I heard her say that a long time ago. But they have not lived with my sister for five years the way I have.

I understand my sister. My sister understands what I say too, especially if I speak slowly and move my hands a lot. But it is not only my lips and fingers that my sister watches.

I wore my sunglasses yesterday. The frames are very large. The lenses are very black. My sister made me take them off when I spoke. What do my brown eyes say to her brown eyes? That I would really rather play ball than play house? That I just heard our mother call, but I do not want to go in yet?

Yes, I have a sister who can understand what I say. But not always. Last night I asked, "Where are my pajamas?" She went into the kitchen and brought out a bunch of bananas from the fruit bowl on the table.

My friends ask me about my little sister. They ask, "Does it hurt to be deaf?" "No," I say, "her ears don't hurt, but her feelings do when people do not understand."

My sister cannot always tell me with words what she feels. Sometimes she cannot even show me with her hands. But when she is angry or happy or sad, my sister can say more with her face and shoulders than anyone else I know.

I tell my friends I have a sister who knows when a dog is barking near her and who says she does not like the feel of that sound. She knows when our cat is purring if it is sitting on her lap, or that our radio is playing if she is touching it with her hand.

63

But my sister will never know if the telephone is ringing or if someone is knocking at the door. She will never hear the garbage cans clanging around in the street.

I have a sister who sometimes cries at night, when it is dark and there is no light in the hall. When I try plugging my ears in the dark, I cannot hear the clock ticking on the shelf or the television playing in the living room. I do not hear any cars moving out on the street. There is nothing. Then I wonder, is it the same?

I have a sister who will never hear the branches scraping against the window of our room. She will not hear the soft music of the wind chimes I have hung up there. But when the storms come, my sister does not wake to the sudden rolling thunder, or to the quick clap-clap of the shutters in the wind. My little sister sleeps. I am the one who is afraid.

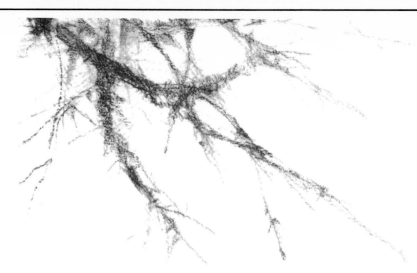

When my friends ask, I tell them I have a sister who watches television without turning on the sound. I have a sister who rocks her dolls without singing any tune. I have a sister who can talk with her fingers or in a hoarse, gentle voice. But sometimes she yells so loud, our mother says the neighbors will complain.

I stamp my foot to get my sister's attention, or wave at her across the room. I come up behind her and put my hand on her arm. She can feel the stamping. She can feel the touching. She can see my moving hand from the corner of her eye. But if I walk up behind her and call out her name, she cannot hear me.

I have a sister.

My sister is deaf.

A Reader Says

I think these two sisters had fun together. I wish I had a sister.

How did you feel about the story?

About the Author

Jeanne Whitehouse Peterson

Jeanne Whitehouse Peterson really has a sister who is deaf. When Mrs. Peterson started writing, she wrote about growing up with her sister. "That's what I knew best," she explains. "I wanted to share the joys and sorrows of the deaf child."

Mrs. Peterson was born in Walla Walla, Washington. When she was twelve, she wrote stories in her uncle's barn. Then she fed the pages to the cows! She is now a schoolteacher as well as a writer. She lives in Albuquerque, New Mexico. She likes reading stories out loud. She also likes hearing others read out loud to her. Some of Peterson's other books are *That is That* and *While the Moon Shines Bright*.

More Books About People

Abby
by Jeannette Caines

In this book you'll meet Abby and find out all about her—where she came from, what was the first thing she said, and what her mother and brother are like.

Happy Birthday, Ronald Morgan!
by Patricia Reilly Giff

Ronald Morgan is back and has some good news and some bad news. The good news is that his birthday is on Friday. The bad news is that school ends one day before that. Will Ronald Morgan be the one boy not to have a happy birthday in class?

Penny
by Beatrice Schenk de Regniers

Penny is a girl who is no bigger than a penny. But, as you'll see, it doesn't keep her from doing things on her own.

MAKING ALL THE
CONNECTIONS

Speaking and Listening

In this part of the book, you read stories about people. You read how Max learned he was good at more than just baseball. You read how Tina felt when her wishes came true. You read how Jenny showed her father that people like to do different things. You read a story about two sisters.

Talk to the other children in your class about the people you read about. You may want to look at your Reader's Log. Say your words clearly when you speak. Listen as the other children talk.

Think about this before you begin. All people are different. Some people are good at tennis. Other people are good at dancing. Some people are funny. Other people like being in plays. What were the people you read about like? Why did you like them?

Thinking About Interviewing Someone

Reading about people is one way of learning about them. Another way is to **interview** them. When you interview a person, you ask questions to find out what that person is like. What person in this part of the book would you like to interview?

For your interview, choose someone you read about and liked.

To do your interview, you will need to follow an **outline**. Write the questions you want to ask on your outline. Leave room for the answers. Then follow the rules on the next page.

Jan's Interview Outline
1. When did you start to play baseball, Max?
2. Do you think learning ballet would be good for all baseball players?

Doing an Interview

Work with a friend. Ask your friend to pretend to be the person you want to interview. Then pretend to be the person your friend wants to interview. When you do your interview try to follow these rules.

1. Think about what you'd like to know about the person you are interviewing.

2. Think of some questions you would like to ask. For example, you might want to ask Max how dancing and playing baseball are the same and how they are different.

3. Write down the questions on your outline.

4. Speak in a clear voice.

5. Be polite.

6. Give the person time to answer.

7. Write the answers down.

8. Leave room at the end of your outline for questions you may think of later.

Have fun asking questions when you do the interview. Have fun pretending to be one of the people in this part of the book.

Sharing Your Interview

You and your friend know who you are going to interview. You have practiced doing an interview. Now remember the rules for interviewing someone, and share your interview with the rest of the class. Here are some ways you can do this.

Doing Your Interview Out Loud

Stand in front of the class. Tell who you are interviewing. Tell the class why you wanted to interview that person. Now do your interview so that the whole class can hear it. Ask your questions in a loud and clear voice so that everyone can hear what you have to say.

Tape Recording Your Interview

Record your interview on a tape recorder. Have the other children in your class listen to how you sound. Then talk about other questions you might have asked. Ask the other children if they have questions for the person you interviewed. Ask them how they would have answered the questions.

PART TWO

Places

This is my rock,
And here I run
To steal the secret of the sun;

This is my rock
And here come I
Before the night has swept the sky;

This is my rock
This is the place
I meet the evening face to face.

This Is My Rock
by David McCord

Some places are as close as home. Others are as far away as the stars. As you read, think: What places do you like?

Using Words About Places

Starting with What You Know

Think about the place you live and the places you have visited. What ideas can you come up with? The words in the box tell about places. Use these words and other words you know to answer the questions after the box.

city	playground	seashore
library	farm	zoo
parking lot	town	park

In what places do people live? Where are places people play? Where do people visit?

Building a Word Map

The word map shows how some of the words in the box above go together. Think about other words you can put on the map.

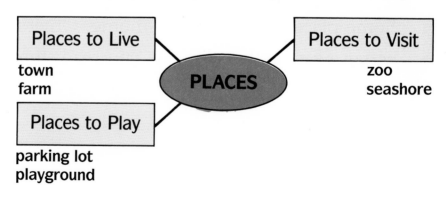

Finishing a Story

Look at the following story. The story tells about places. Some words are left out. Think of the words you would use to finish the story. Use the words from the box and word map in this lesson for ideas. Complete the story.

Danny lives in the ＿＿. Here, there are many places to play. Danny likes to play in the ＿＿. Danny would like to visit the ＿＿.

Rosa lives in the ＿＿. She likes to play in the ＿＿. One day Rosa would like to visit the ＿＿. She would have a good time there.

Share your story with your class. What words did the children in your class use? How were the stories different?

As You Read

In this part of the book, you will read about places. Keep a Reader's Log. A Reader's Log will help you remember thoughts, ideas, and new words. Start the log with the word map. Write the new words on your map as you find them.

In this story, a girl finds her own place to think, read, and dream. Read on to find out why this place is special to her.

In My Treehouse

by Alice Schertle

When I'm up high in my treehouse I'm all alone. Just me, myself, and I. On a crook of a nearby branch, a place just right for a bird nest, I hung a shoelace, some string, a piece of rag, and some of my hair. But no bird has made a nest here yet. Sometimes I wonder if the birds think I'm another bird. Maybe they think that my treehouse is a giant nest, and one nest in this tree is enough.

When I'm in my treehouse I think about things. I think about riding a roller coaster, about a dream I had, about being the strongest person in the world, and about being invisible. I think about flying an airplane, taming a lion, and having an elephant for a pet.

On sunny days, I might haul a bucket of books into my treehouse. I make a nice, soft corner with an old bunched-up bedspread. I sink down into it and read. Just me, myself, and I. And a hundred books or so.

Once I spent the night in my treehouse. I used our old brown sleeping bag that smells like the garage. I found out that lots of things make noises at night, and it's too dark to see what's out there. So I was glad when my cat came up to sleep with me. Her purr is so loud you can hardly hear anything else.

In my treehouse I can lie on my back and look up through leaves. I can listen to birds. I can curl up and read. I can do all these things in my treehouse. Just me, myself, and I.

Thinking About the Theme

1. What were some things that the girl in the story liked to do in her treehouse?

2. What are some special places that you like?

Understanding Order in a Story

for **The Boy Who Saved Holland** and **The Best New Thing**

What did José do first? What did he do next? What did he do last?

Thinking About Order

All stories have **order**. Words such as *first*, *next*, *then*, and *last* are clues to the order. Read this story. What is the order? What clues help you?

Donna was dressing up to be in the play. First she put on some makeup. Then she put on a big, red nose. Finally, she put on a funny hat.

As You Read

As you read the two stories that follow, ask yourself this question. "In what order are things happening?" Use the notes in blue to help you.

People have strong feelings for the places where they live. Peter loved his land so much he saved it—using just one finger.

The Boy Who Saved Holland

by Mary Mapes Dodge

Long ago there was a boy named Peter who lived in a land called Holland. Peter knew that Holland was a very special place. There was so much to see. Peter loved nothing more than walking in the country.

The land in Holland was low and flat. Bright tulips grew everywhere. There were slowly turning windmills. There were high walls called dikes.

This tells what Holland is like.

Peter knew Holland needed dikes because the land was lower than the sea in some places. If the dikes broke, the sea would flood the land.

Dikes are needed in Holland.

Peter loved to take his walks after school. He liked to walk by himself and enjoy the slowly turning windmills. He liked to watch people planting the tulip bulbs. But the walk he liked the most took him to the top of the dikes. From there he could see far over the country.

He would stand on top of the dike and feel its strength. The dike kept back the water. He knew the dike kept the land he loved safe from the sea.

One day while Peter was walking, he thought, "Today I want to see everything."

He hurried far down the road to the dikes. He ran to the top.

"There's so much to see from up here," thought Peter. He saw windmills turning and many bright tulips everywhere. He was very happy, but he knew it was time to go home.

Just as Peter started to go home, he heard a strange sound. First he listened and looked around. Then he saw where the sound was coming from. Water was coming out of a hole in the dike. There was a leak in the dike!

Next Peter hurried to the leak. There was no one around to help him. He was by himself, so he had to do something on his own. He knew that the leak could get bigger and bigger and then the dike would break. The sea would flood the land.

Finally Peter knew what he must do. With all his strength, he put his finger in the hole to plug up the leak. Now Holland would be safe from a flood.

Peter starts to do something. The clue word helps you know the order.

Think of what Peter will do.

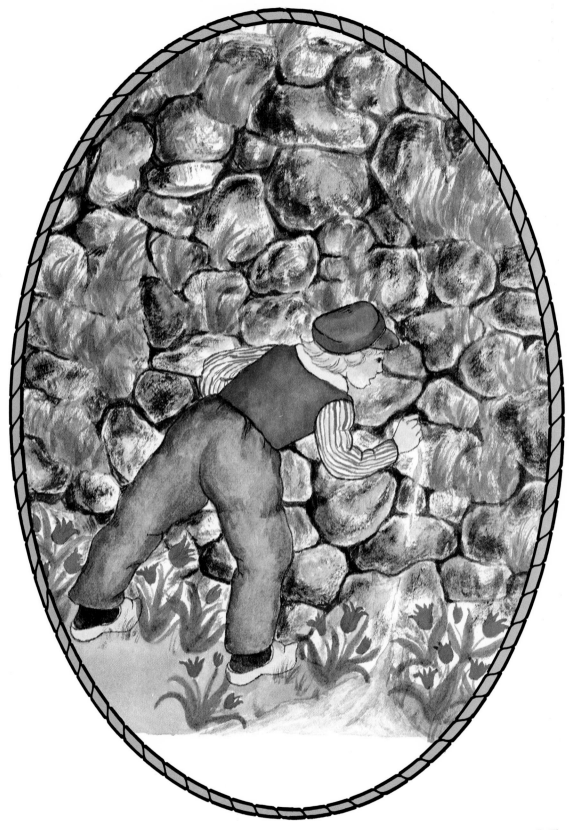

Peter stood there for a long time, but no
one came by to help. He grew very tired and
afraid. His strength was going, but he kept
his finger in the leak. The time passed very,
very slowly for Peter.

After a while, he heard someone coming
down the road in a cart. It was a man. He
came closer and closer.

"Help, help!" shouted Peter.

The man in the cart stopped his horse and
hurried over to Peter. "Are you all right?"
asked the man.

Think of how the
man could help
him.

"There's a leak in the dike! I have my
finger in the hole to plug up the leak. We
must stop the leak or there will be a flood!

Please go for help. My strength is running out, so hurry, please!"

The man ran back to his cart, turned his horse around, and hurried back to town.

Peter waited and waited. He couldn't wait much longer. Then from far down the road he heard a new sound. He heard talking and shouting. The people from the town were coming to help!

Think about the kind of person Peter is.

First they fixed the leak. Then everyone thanked Peter for his help. They knew that his quick thinking had saved the town and the land. Finally they shouted, "Peter saved Holland! Peter is a hero!"

The clue words show the order.

Peter smiled, but he did not feel like a hero. He was just tired and very happy that everyone was safe.

Today Holland is still a special place. There are tulips and windmills and dikes to hold back the sea. People still plant the bulbs that grow into bright tulips. And to this day, Peter is a hero and still is called the boy who saved Holland.

A Reader Says

Peter was very brave. I would like to do something brave for my country.

How did you feel about the story?

After You Read

Thinking About What You Read

1. Why did Peter like the dikes?

2. Why was it hard for Peter to keep his finger in the hole for so long?

3. What might have happened if Peter hadn't put his finger in the dike when he saw there was a leak?

4. Why did people say Peter was a hero?

Thinking About How You Read

How did thinking about order help you understand what Peter did?

Sharing and Listening

Tell what you think it means to be a hero. Then tell if you thought Peter was a hero. Why or why not? Listen as other people give their ideas.

Writing

Peter loved to take walks after school because there was so much to see. Write a few sentences about something you like to see when you walk home from school.

Have you ever looked at a star and thought about what it would be like to go to a new planet? In this story, a girl visits Earth and finds out the thing she likes best about it.

The Best New Thing

by Isaac Asimov

Rada lived on a little world, far out in space. Her father and her mother and her brother, Jonathan, lived there too.

Rada was the only little girl on the little world. Jonny was the only little boy. Rada's father and mother worked on the spaceships. They looked to see that everything was all right before the spaceships went on their way back to Earth or to other planets. Rada and Jonny would watch the ships come and go.

Rada and Jonny had to wear their spacesuits when they watched. There was no air on the little world, but inside their suits there was air and it was warm.

When people came out of the spaceships, they saw Rada and Jonny. One man said, "Would you like to see Earth someday?"

Jonny asked, "Are things different on Earth?"

"Well, the sky is blue," said the man.

"I have never seen a blue sky," said Rada.

"There is air on Earth. You don't have to wear a spacesuit," he said.

Rada said, "That must be nice. I will ask my father if I can go to Earth."

She jumped high to see where her father was. She jumped so high, she could see all around the spaceship. She did not see her father.

She pulled a little ring on her suit. That made her go down again. She came down very near the man.

The man said, "That is well done, but you could not do that on Earth."

Rada said, "Why not?"

"On Earth," said the man, "you can only jump a little way. Earth pulls you down right away. And you roll down any slanting place."

Then the man had to go into the spaceship again. Rada and Jonny waited for their father.

When their father came, Rada and Jonny went underground with him. Rada and Jonny and their father and mother lived inside the little world, in nice, large rooms.

Jonny said, "Dad, is it true that you don't have to wear a space suit on Earth?"

His father said, "Yes, it is. There is air on Earth."

Jonny said, "And is the sky really blue there?"

"That's right," his father answered. "And there are white things in the sky called clouds. Sometimes drops of water come from the sky. That is rain."

Rada thought about this, and then she said, "If the ground has water on it, don't people slip and fall?"

Her father laughed, and then he said, "The rain doesn't stay on top of the ground. It sinks into the ground and helps to make the grass grow."

"Will we go to Earth someday, Dad?"

"Yes, Rada," her father said. "Maybe we can go soon."

"Have I ever been there, Dad?" asked Rada.

"Yes," said her father. "You were born there, but you can't remember it because you were only a baby. And Jonny wasn't even born."

Rada and Jonny could not sleep that night. There were so many new things on Earth to think about. There was air that was everywhere. There were the blue sky and the rain, the wind and the flowers. And there were even birds and animals.

But there was one new thing Rada really wanted to do. She told Jonny about it and he wanted to do it too. They didn't tell their father or mother. It was something they had never done before. On Earth, they were going to find out what it felt like.

One day a spaceship came and their father said, "This is the ship that will take us to Earth."

Rada felt a little bit sad. She would miss her little world. When they were getting into the spaceship, she turned and said, "I'm leaving now, little world. It is time for me to go to Earth. But I'll always remember you."

Then the spaceship started to move.

Rada could see the little world as the ship moved away from it. Soon it was just a dot and then all Rada could see were the stars.

"Can we see Earth, Dad?" Jonny asked.

"It looks like a star from here. It's that bright one there," said his father.

"Look at Earth, Rada," said Jonny.

Rada looked at the bright star and was happy. Soon she would be on Earth and would know about the new thing. She knew Jonny was thinking about it, too.

When the ship stopped, Rada took off her belt. She was the first one to get out of the chair. Jonny was next.

"Aren't we going to put on our space suits?" asked Rada.

"Don't forget, we don't have to put on space suits on Earth," said her father.

"Yes," said Rada. "That's one of the new things." She and Jonny were waiting for another new thing, too. They held each other's hand but they didn't say anything.

They all walked out of the ship. It was warm and the sun was very big.

"What is that sound?" asked Rada.

"It is a bird singing," said her mother.

Rada had never heard a bird singing. She had never felt the wind. She had never seen such a big sun and such bright sunlight.

These were all new things.

Now it was time for the best new thing of all.

She said, "Come on, Jonny."

Jonny said, "Look at the grass. And there's a little hill. Let's try it."

They ran to the little hill. Then they rolled down the hill. When they were done, they stood up, laughing.

Their father and mother came to them.

"You can't run like that here," said their mother.

"But we wanted to," said Rada. "We are so happy because we know, now, about the new thing."

"What new thing?" asked her father.

"We rolled down the hill," said Rada. "I think it's the best new thing of all."

"Yes," said Jonny. "It is!"

And they ran up to the top of the hill to try it again.

A Reader Says

I would like to visit Rada's home. I would like to go to a place where there's no gravity.

How did you feel about the story?

After You Read

Thinking About What You Read

1. How could Rada jump so high? Why did she pull a little ring to come down?

2. Why hadn't the children ever seen a blue sky, or birds?

3. How did Rada and Johnny feel about visiting Earth?

4. Why did the children laugh after they rolled down a hill?

Thinking About How You Read

Think about Rada in the end of the story. Things happen in order in a story. How did knowing that help you understand why Rada knew so little about Earth?

Sharing and Listening

Tell what you think Johnny and Rada liked and did not like about living in space. Listen as other children give their ideas.

Writing

Pretend you are going to Rada's world. Write a few sentences telling what would be the "best new thing" you would do there.

Watching the Stars

In the story *The Best New Thing*, Rada lived on a planet in outer space. She thought about what it would be like to visit Earth. To her, Earth was very far away.

When you look at the night sky, you can see many stars in the sky. Have you ever thought about them? You cannot visit a star, but you can learn to pick out a few of them.

The Big Dipper is a group of seven stars that looks like a big spoon, or dipper, with a long handle. It is easy to find. Just go outside on a clear night and face north.

You can see the Big Dipper best in the summer. In the summer the Big Dipper is high in the sky. In the winter the Big Dipper is lower in the sky and is a little harder to see.

The Little Dipper is also a group of stars. It looks like a small spoon or dipper with a handle. You can use the Big Dipper to find it. Just make a line with your finger from the two stars at the bottom of the Big Dipper. This line points to a very bright star called the North Star. The North Star is over the North Pole and always points north. It is the first star in the handle of the Little Dipper.

The Big Dipper and the Little Dipper are just two of the many star groups you can see. Next time you look at the night sky, see if you can find them.

Afternoon
on a Hill

I will be the gladdest thing
   Under the sun!
I will touch a hundred flowers
   And not pick one.

I will look at cliffs and clouds
   With quiet eyes,
Watch the wind bow down the grass,
   And the grass rise.

And when lights begin to show
   Up from the town,
I will mark which must be mine,
   And then start down!

Edna St. Vincent Millay

Understanding
Stories That Give Facts

Starting with What You Know

Things that are true are called **facts**. Your name is a fact. How old you are is a fact. What other facts do you know?

Thinking About Stories That Give Facts

Some stories are true. These stories give facts about real people, real places, and real things. When you read a true story, it helps to think of questions that the story might answer. This will help you as you read the story. Then, read the story to find the facts that answer your questions. You may have to read more slowly. There may be new ideas to think about.

As You Read

As you read the two stories that follow, ask yourself this question. "What questions can I ask that will help me find the facts?" Use the notes in blue to help you.

Have you ever sailed in a boat? Flown in a plane? These are just two ways that people travel from place to place.

TRANSPORTATION

by Martin Oshiro

This tells you what transportation is.

Transportation is the way people get from one place to another, and the way people send things from one place to another. Transportation has helped towns and cities grow.

Now you know three ways to travel.

There are three ways to travel—by land, water, and air. People most often use cars, trains, and trucks on land, and use ships and boats on water. But when going to a place far away, people often use airplanes.

Transportation is faster than it was in the past because of the invention of the steam engine. Before it was invented in the 1700s, all ships had sails and needed the help of the wind to move. With the steam engine, ships could move faster than ever before.

Trains were invented after the steam engine. Trains used the steam engine, also. By the end of the 1800s, it was easy for people to travel across America by train in less than a week. Today that doesn't seem very fast. But before steam engines, the trip could take weeks by horse and wagon.

Train travel also made it easier to send food and clothes from one part of the country to another. A train could carry more than horses pulling a wagon could carry. And because the train could get to different parts of the country faster, the food would stay fresh.

Think of a question about trains. Look for an answer as you read this paragraph.

Soon an engine that ran on gas was invented. The gas engine was clean and easy to use. Two inventions that used the gas engine were the car and the airplane. They made it easier for people to travel faster.

Cars were invented at the end of the 1800s. But not many people owned one then because cars sold for a lot of money.

In the 1900s a way was found to make cars so they could be sold for less. Soon, many people owned them. Now most people use cars as transportation.

The invention of the airplane made transportation faster, also. Before the airplane was invented, the only way to travel across the sea was by ship, which sometimes took weeks. With the airplane, people could go across the sea in less than one day.

In the 1930s the invention of the jet engine made air travel faster than ever. Today a trip across America takes very little time by jet.

Today rockets can travel to the moon and far out in space to help us learn more about space.

Think of something faster than an airplane.

Ships were slow.

Think about why people will go into space.

It's hard to believe that someday people may go into space as often as they fly on an airplane today. But remember, once it was hard to believe that anyone could get off the ground and fly at all.

A Reader Says

One day I'd like to take a trip in a rocket ship.

How did you feel about the story?

After You Read

Thinking About What You Read

1. How did the invention of the steam engine help people?

2. Why don't very many people use sailing ships to go across the sea now?

3. How would we travel if the gas engine had not been invented?

4. How can modern transportation help cities grow?

Thinking About How You Read

How did asking questions about transportation as you were reading help you to understand the story?

Sharing and Listening

Today people can travel to different places fast. What do you think life was like in the past when transportation was not so fast? Tell your ideas to the children in your class. Listen as they share their ideas.

Writing

What are some other ways to travel? Pick one. Write a few sentences about why it is a good way to travel.

People have traveled to many places in outer space. But no one lives in space—yet. Have you ever thought about what it would be like to live in space?

The Newest Cities of All

by Judy Rosenbaum

People today live in some unusual places. There are towns on top of mountains. There are homes in dry deserts. Some people even live in houses under the ground.

Someday, we may live in even stranger places than these. We may have cities under the sea. We may put up homes at the South Pole. Or we may build towns in outer space.

We already fly into space. People have walked on our moon. Astronauts have spent weeks living in space. Right now, a space ship with no people in it is flying to the planet Pluto. One day, more people will travel in space. Some will go there to live. They will face some new problems.

Where in space would we build a city?
The moon looks like a good place. It is the
space body closest to Earth. We might also
try Mars. Mars is one of the nearest planets
to Earth. We could also build city-ships right
in space. These city-ships would never land.
They would just keep floating.

Many things will be the same about life in
space. We will still need to eat and sleep. We
will need and want to play, sing, tell stories,
and be with friends. We will not stop doing
these things just because we are in space.
But we may do some things in a new way.

Think about what is different in space. There is no air in space or on other planets we have found. There is no water. No plants grow. People can't live without air or water. They also need to grow food to eat.

How could we have air and water in space? We would have to carry them along with us in big tanks on the flight. We already do this in spaceships. On a planet or moon, we might build a big dome. This dome would go over a city and keep the air in. Maybe someday we will find a way to make air and water from things in space.

Today, space travelers take special food along on space ships. It is dried into little packs. But who would really want to live on dried food for a long time in a space city? It would be much better to grow food right near the city. We would have to take Earth plants along with us to plant there. We might not need to take soil with us, however. There is a new way to grow plants without soil. People can now put plants into water with special plant foods in it. Maybe this would be better than soil for growing plants in space. All that soil would be hard to carry in a space ship. It would take up too much room in the ship, too.

Having to carry everything from Earth will be one of the biggest problems in space. There seems to be no life on the moon and most planets. All they have is rock. Rock can be used for building homes. But all other things will need to be flown in. This means *everything*—clothes, beds, glass for windows, even paper. People in space cities will need to take care of how they use things. They might find more ways to use things over and over and not throw them away. This is called *recycling*. Air will have to be recycled. So will some water. How could people recycle things like cloth and paper? How do we do this today on Earth?

People in space will want to talk to their friends on Earth. This will not be a big problem. We already know how to talk to each other across space. Do you remember seeing space flights on your T.V. screen? The astronauts talked to Earth. People on Earth could even watch on their T.V. screens astronauts moving around on the moon.

Maybe you will get to live in a space city one day. What do you think your life will be like? What will the streets look like? Will people ride bikes and skate down those streets? What kinds of clothes will people wear? What new machines will these cities hold? Will space cities look like the make-believe space cities you see on T.V.?

115

One day you may find out. You may even be one of the people who helps build such a city. One day, children may open a book a lot like this one. Inside will be a story about cities in space. And next to the story will be the face of someone living in that city—you.

A Reader Says

I would like to visit space, but I think I would miss Earth after a while.

How did you feel about the story?

After You Read

Thinking About What You Read

1. What would be the biggest problems about living in space?

2. Why would we have to find new ways to grow food?

3. Why would people in a space city use things over and over again?

4. Why might people someday live in space?

Thinking About How You Read

How did asking questions about cities in outer space help you find the facts?

Sharing and Listening

Tell why you think people might really live in space someday, or why not? Listen as other people give their ideas.

Writing

Write to a friend on Earth from your home in a space city. Tell what new things you have been doing.

Evan dreams of having a place he can call his own. But is being by yourself the same as being happy?

Evan's Corner

◆

by Elizabeth Starr Hill

Evan walked home from school slowly. He stopped in front of a pet shop.

In the window, a canary sang to him from its golden cage. That canary has its own cage, Evan thought. *I* want a place of my own.

He walked on. A bright pink flower on a window sill caught his eye. That flower has its own pot, he thought. I wish *I* had a place of my own.

He crossed the noisy, busy street and turned into the building where he and his family lived.

Soon his three sisters and his two brothers would come home. Then his mother and then his father.

Such a big family, Evan thought. And no place to call just *mine*.

Evan wore a door key around his neck so he could unlock the door. Usually he was the first one home. But today the door flew open before he touched it.

"Surprise!" his mother said as she stood there laughing. "I beat you home, Evan!"

Evan gave his mother a big hug. He liked it when she got home ahead of him. Now they could have a private talk before his brothers and sisters came in.

"Mama, you know what I am wishing for *hard*?" Evan said.

"Tell me." His mother smiled.

Evan told her the canary bird had a cage. He told her the flower had a pot. He said, "And Mama, *I* want a place of my own."

His mother thought and thought. At first it seemed she might not find a way. But then her face lighted up and she said, "Each one of us in the family can have a corner. You have first choice, Evan."

Evan ran to every corner of the rooms. The one Evan liked best, the one he wanted for his own, had a nice small window and a nice shiny floor.

That night he sat alone on the floor, in his corner.

His little brother Adam asked him, "Why do you want a corner of your own, Evan?"

Evan thought and then said, "I want a chance to be lonely."

Adam tiptoed away.

Later Adam tiptoed up to Evan and said, "Are you being lonely now?"

"No," Evan said. "I'm wasting time. In my own way. In my own corner."

Adam asked, "Can I ever come into your corner, Evan?"

"Why don't you choose a corner of your own?" Evan said.

So Adam did. He chose the corner across the room from Evan's. He sat in it. He called, "What shall I do in my corner, Evan?"

"Whatever you like," Evan said.

But Adam didn't know what to do. After a minute he left his corner. He played horse with his big sister Lucy. He sat on her back and held on to her pigtails. "Gid-yup, Lucy-horse!" he shouted. They galloped round and round the room.

The next morning, Evan got up and ran to his corner. His floor was shiny as ever. It was still fun to look out his window.

But Evan felt that his corner needed something more.

What could it be?

He stared at the bare walls. I know! he thought. I need a picture! And I'll make it myself!

In school that morning, Evan painted a picture of the sea. He drew big waves and a green boat.

He told his teacher, "I'm going to hang this picture in my own corner!"

"That will be lovely, Evan," his teacher said.

Evan could hardly wait to get home after school. He ran past the pet shop.

"Canary bird!" he shouted over his shoulder. "I've got a place of my own now! I'm going to hang a picture in it!"

A-skip and a-gallop, he passed the window sill with the flower pot.

"Listen, old pink flower," he told it. "I've got a place of my own and I made a picture for it!"

He skidded to a stop at the corner. He waited for the light to change. He spoke to the man at the newsstand. "Guess what, mister!"

"What, little boy?"

"I'm going to hang this picture in a place that's *just mine!*"

And he skipped and rushed and almost flew the rest of the way.

He taped the picture to the wall beside the window in his corner. He stepped back to look at it.

The green boat seemed to bob on the blue waves. It bobbed too much. Evan realized the picture was crooked.

He straightened it. Now it looked just right.

Soon Adam came home and he saw Evan's picture. "That's pretty, Evan!" he said. "Do you think I could draw a picture for my corner?"

"Sure you could."

Adam ran off. But he could not find any paper or crayons. Lucy, his sister, had some, but she was busy with homework now.

He came back to Evan.

Evan sat in his corner with his back to the room. He looked up at his picture.

Adam asked Evan, "Are you being lonely, Evan?"

"No," Evan said.

"Are you wasting your own time in your own way?"

"No," Evan told him.

"Well then, what are you doing?"

"Enjoying peace and quiet," Evan said.

Adam tiptoed off.

That night, Evan did not sleep well. He lay awake in bed, thinking about his corner.

It had a nice floor and a nice window and a nice picture. But was that enough?

No, he decided finally. I need something more.

But what?

He thought about the pink flower in its pot. He thought: That's it! I need a plant of my own, in my own corner.

On Saturday, Evan went across the street to the playground. He took his toothbrush, glass, and a spoon.

Evan found a weed that had big flowers on it. He dug it up with his spoon. He planted it in his glass.

Then he took it home and put it on the windowsill, in his own corner. But still his corner didn't seem right, and he didn't know why.

I don't have any furniture, he realized at last. Why didn't I think of that before?

He ran to the store and asked Mr. Meehan for two old crates. Mr. Meehan let him have the crates.

In his corner, Evan stood one of the crates up on end. Now it was like a high desk. He turned the other crate over to make a bench and he sat on it.

Now Evan had many things.

He had a place of his own. He could be lonely there. He could waste time if he liked. He could enjoy peace and quiet.

He had a fine picture to look at.

He had a bench of his own to sit on, by his own window. His plant grew tall.

Evan spent most of his spare time in his corner. But—it was strange. He just was not happy.

When his mother came home, Evan said, "Mama, I'm not happy in my corner. What do I need now?"

Together she and Evan stood off from the corner and looked at it.

Evan's corner was beautiful. They could see that.

"Evan," his mother said at last, "maybe what you need is to leave your corner for a while. Just fixing up your own corner is nice, but maybe you need to step out now, and help someone else."

She left him, and he sat alone on his bench, thinking it over.

Adam came in and asked, "Are you enjoying peace and quiet, Evan?"

Evan said, "No, I'm going to get some crayons to help you draw a picture. I'm going to help you fix up your corner so it's the best corner in the world!"

A look of joy came over Adam's face—and over Evan's.

They ran across the room together to work on Adam's corner.

A Reader Says

I think Evan was being mean at first. He didn't help or play with his little brother.

How did you feel about the story?

About the Author

Elizabeth Starr Hill

Elizabeth Starr Hill was born in Florida. Her best-known children's book is *Evan's Corner*. She also wrote *The Wonderful Visit to Miss Liberty*, *Pardon My Fangs*, and *Ever-After Island*.

Mrs. Hill thinks that "writers should know how things look and sound and smell and feel." Then they will write so that readers can enjoy the story.

She believes that stories are everywhere and that all you have to do is listen to the world around you and you will find your own stories.

Mrs. Hill now enjoys living in the country.

More Books About Places

My Two Feet *by Alice Schertle*
You don't need a boat or a plane or a spaceship to take you to special places. In this book, you'll meet a girl who goes to many different places all year round—just by using her own two feet!

The House on East Eighty-Eighth Street
by Bernard Waber
Is a house in the city really the right place for Lyle the Crocodile to live in? You'll find out when you read this book.

The Desert Is Theirs
by Byrd Baylor
This book will show you how the desert is more than just a dry place where it never rains. You'll see that the desert is a special place. And you'll meet the many birds, animals, plants, and people who call the desert their home.

MAKING ALL THE
CONNECTIONS

Speaking and Listening

In this part of the book, you read about some special places. You read about Holland and how Peter saved it. You read how Rada went to a new place and did a special new thing. You even read how people go from one place to another. You read about how Evan wanted a special place of his own and what he learned when he had this place.

Take turns talking about the stories with the other children in your class. You may want to look at your Reader's Log. Think before you speak. Listen when other people talk.

Before you begin, think about this. Everyone has a special place. Some people like to be outside. Other people have a special room. What are the special places in the stories you have read? Why are these places special?

Reading Something New in Social Studies

What is the smallest state in the United States? It is Rhode Island. Here is a story about something Rhode Island did that was very important to our history.

Over two hundred years ago, Rhode Island was not a state. The United States was not a country. We belonged to a country called England. People from England came to America. They started places called colonies. There were thirteen of these colonies. Rhode Island was one of them.

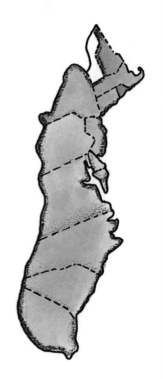

The rules for the colonies were made by the king of England. The people in the colonies wanted to make their own rules. The king would not be happy to hear this. The people of Rhode Island were not afraid. They were the first ones to tell the king that they wanted to rule themselves! Soon all of the other colonies did the same thing, but the smallest was first!

MAKING ALL THE CONNECTIONS

Thinking About Places

The story you just read told about a special place: Rhode Island. The stories you read in this part of the book told about other kinds of special places. Think about all the places you read about. Fill in the chart. Tell why each place is special.

Place	Why It Is Special
Rhode Island	
The Tree House	
Holland	
Evan's Corner	

You have read stories about different places. You have read why the people in the stories thought the places were special. Do you have a special place of your own? Why is it special? Write the name of that place in the chart. Maybe you can write about it.

Writing About a Special Place

You have read stories about people and their special places. Now it is your turn to write about a place that is special to you. Before you write about your place, look at the story *In My Treehouse* on page 78 in this book. In this story a girl tells about her own special place. Then follow these steps.

Planning

Think about your special place, then draw a picture of it. Below your picture, write some notes that tell about the place. Here are Len's picture and two notes about his special place.

It is cool.
It is dark.

MAKING ALL THE CONNECTIONS

Writing

Use your picture and the notes you wrote to write the answers to these questions:

1. Where is my special place?

2. What things do I like to do in my special place?

3. What do I like best about my place?

4. How does my special place make me feel?

Here are Len's answers to the questions.

1. My place is under the slide.
2. I like to sit and read there. I even like to eat my lunch there.
3. It is cool and dark.
4. I feel happy there.

Checking

When you are finished writing the answers to the questions, it is time to check your story. Ask yourself these questions.

- Did I begin each sentence with a capital letter?
- Did I always write the word **I** with a capital letter?
- Did I end each sentence with an end mark?

  Make any changes that you need to make.

Sharing Your Story

After you have finished checking your work, you can share your story with your classmates. Here are two ways to share your story.

- Read your story out loud to the class. Say your words clearly. Listen closely as other people read their stories.
- Show the picture you made of your special place. Tell the class about the things you put in the picture.

PART THREE

Great Creatures

Elephants walking
Along the trails

Are holding hands
By holding tails . . .

from *Holding Hands*
by Lenore M. Link

◆

Great creatures can be big animals. They can also be animals who do great things. In this part of the book you'll meet many different kinds of creatures, from dinosaurs to cats. As you read, think: What makes each of these animals great?

141

Using Words About Great Creatures

Starting with What You Know

Think about great creatures. What ideas can you come up with? The words in the box tell about great creatures. Use these words to answer the questions after the box.

whale	forest	sea
land	elephant	large
lion	big	scary

What are some great creatures? What words would you use to write about them? Where might a great creature live?

Building a Word Map

The word map shows how some of the words in the box above go together. Think about words you can put on the map.

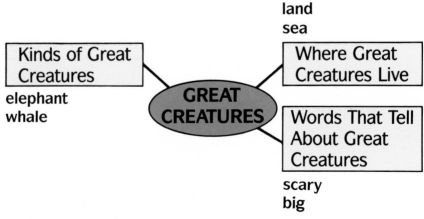

land
sea

Kinds of Great Creatures

Where Great Creatures Live

elephant
whale

GREAT CREATURES

Words That Tell About Great Creatures

scary
big

Finishing a Story

Look at the following story. The story tells about a great creature. Some words are left out. Think of the words you would use to finish the story. Use the words from the box and word map in this lesson for ideas. Complete the story.

Lucky was a ＿＿＿. Lucky lived in the ＿＿＿. He was a very ＿＿＿ animal. Lucky once visited his friend, Margo. Margo was a ＿＿＿. She lived in the ＿＿＿. She was a ＿＿＿ animal. Lucky and Margo ate lunch together. It was a ＿＿＿ lunch!

Share your story with your class. What words did the children in your class use? How were the stories different?

As You Read

In this part of the book, you will read about great creatures. Keep a Reader's Log. A Reader's Log will help you remember thoughts, ideas, and new words. Start the log with the word map. Write new words on your map as you find them.

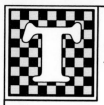

Little Gorilla knows that everyone likes him when he's little. But what will happen once he begins to grow?

Little GORILLA

◆

by Ruth Bornstein

Once there was a little gorilla, and everybody loved him. His mother loved him. His father loved him. His grandmother and grandfather loved him. Everyone loved him.

Even when he was only one day old, everybody loved Little Gorilla.

Pink Butterfly flying in the forest, Green Parrot in his tree, and Red Monkey in her tree, all loved Little Gorilla. Even Big Boa Constrictor thought Little Gorilla was nice.

Giraffe, walking in the forest, was there when Little Gorilla needed him. Little Elephant, and Big Elephant too, came to see him.

Lion roared his loudest roar for him. Even Old Hippo took him wherever he wanted to go, because she loved Little Gorilla.

Just about everybody in the great green forest loved Little Gorilla! Then one day something happened . . .

Little Gorilla began to grow and Grow and Grow and GROW.

And one day, Little Gorilla became BIG!
And everybody came, and everybody sang
"Happy birthday! Happy birthday Little
Gorilla!   Happy birthday to you!"
And everybody still loved him.

Thinking About the Theme

1. Do you think Little Gorilla was afraid of
growing bigger?

2. All his friends liked Little Gorilla while he
was a small creature. How did they feel
about him when he became a great creature?

Understanding the Big Idea

What is the picture about?

Thinking About the Big Idea

A story tells you about people, animals, and places. It tells you about things that happen. Most stories have a big idea. It is what the story is all about. Read this story. What is it all about?

Andy and Cathy saw many animals at the zoo. They saw a giraffe and an elephant. They watched the seals playing in the water. Andy pointed to a lion. The lion was sleeping.

As You Read

As you read the two stories that follow, ask yourself this question. "What is the story all about?" Use the notes in blue to help you.

Can an alligator talk? Read on to find out how some great creatures, such as alligators, talk to each other.

What Is That Alligator Saying?

by Ruth Belov Gross

People can tell each other things in a lot of different ways. They can do it by talking. And they can tell each other things without talking at all. They can use their hands. They can make faces. They can make funny sounds. They can cry.

Animals have ways of telling each other things, too. Sometimes we say they are talking to each other. But animals do not talk the way we do. They communicate in a special way.

Some animals do things that other animals can see. Some animals do things that other animals can feel. Some animals make sounds that other animals can hear. Some animals make smells other animals can smell.

Many kinds of baby animals cannot do things on their own. They need their mothers to feed them and to keep them safe.

These baby creatures have special ways to tell their mothers when they are hungry or in danger. And their mothers have special ways to warn the babies when there is danger.

Baby alligators communicate with their mothers by grunting. Whenever a mother alligator hears her babies grunting—*umph, umph, umph*—she comes to them right away.

The first time an alligator hears her babies, she is not able to see them. Their little grunts are coming from a bunch of old leaves and some mud. That is where the mother alligator laid her eggs many weeks ago.

Now the mother alligator goes to the bunch of leaves. She digs it open with her long alligator snout. And there, under the leaves, are her babies! She helps them get out of their muddy nest.

If baby alligators couldn't communicate with their mother, what would happen? The mother alligator might forget to dig them out with her snout.

Mother alligators also communicate with their babies by grunting. *Umph, umph, umph*—a mother alligator is warning her babies that danger is near. The babies hide in the water when they hear this sound.

If a mother alligator couldn't warn her babies of danger, what would happen to them?

Animals cannot say "Watch out!" the way we can. They have their own ways of warning each other that danger may be near.

A beaver uses its tail to say "Watch out!" It brings its tail up over its back. Then it smacks its tail *hard* on the water of the beaver pond.

Think about what would happen if a beaver saw a hungry bear.

The sound can be heard far away. It tells other beavers that danger is near.

When the other beavers hear the smacking sound, they dive into the pond. But first they smack *their* tails on the water.

Smack! Whack! Smack! The beavers are passing the danger warning to other beavers around the pond.

Look for details about "Crow Talk" as you read on.

Some birds make a lot of noise. Crows go *caw, caw, caw* a lot, and they make other noises, too.

Hubert Frings and his wife Mable Frings are two people who studied "crow talk." They wanted to find out how crows tell each other, "Watch out—danger! Fly away as fast as you can!" So they hid microphones near a bunch of crows.

After a while they had a lot of different crow sounds. Then they played the sounds back to the crows. They played the sounds one at a time.

152

They played the first sound back to the crows. Nothing happened. They played another sound, and again nothing happened.

Then they tried a third sound. When they played this sound, crows came flying from all over.

They tried one more crow sound—and this time all the crows flew away! The crows flew away every time that sound was played.

Now they knew which sound meant "watch out—fly away." They named this the "alarm call."

And they also knew which sound made the crows come together. They named this the "assembly call."

This story tells you some things about how animals communicate. But there is a lot more to know. If you want to, you can find out more by reading.

You can also find out more about how animals communicate by watching what animals do. You can watch flies and ants, and you can watch cats and birds.

Maybe you will find out something that no one knew before.

A Reader Says

I never knew that the sounds animals made were more than just noise!

How did you feel about the story?

After You Read

Thinking About What You Read

1. What are some ways animals can talk to each other?

2. Why do beavers smack their tails in place of using their voices?

3. How did the Frings know that they understood what the crows were saying?

4. Why do animals communicate with each other?

Thinking About How You Read

How did asking yourself what the story was about help you understand it?

Sharing and Listening

Tell which facts you liked the most in this story. Which animals would you like to know more about? Listen as others tell what they liked the most.

Writing

Write the ways that alligators, crows, and beavers talk. Then write about other animals you know and the ways they might communicate.

The largest creatures ever to live were dinosaurs. Dinosaurs died out, but you can see their bones in museums around the world. Read on to find out how we know about the way these great creatures lived.

DIGGING UP DINOSAURS

by Aliki

And putting them together again.

Dinosaurs lived millions of years ago. A few of them were as small as birds, but most were very big.

IGUANODON
PLANT-EATER

Some dinosaurs ate plants. Some dinosaurs ate the meat of other dinosaurs, and some ate the eggs of other dinosaurs.

Dinosaurs lived everywhere. They lived in every part of the world.

Then they died out. No one knows for sure why they became extinct. But they did. There hasn't been a dinosaur on earth for 65 million years.

Until about 200 years ago, no one knew about dinosaurs at all. Then people began finding things buried in rock. They found large footprints. They found very big bones.

People were finding fossils. Fossils are a way of learning about the past. They are all that is left of plants and animals that died long ago. Instead of falling apart, the plants and animals slowly turned to stone.

People found more and more big bones in different parts of the world. Scientists studied the fossils. They said the bones were part of giant reptiles that lived on earth for millions of years. The giants were named DINOSAURIA, or TERRIBLE LIZARD.

What finds these were!

People went to museums to see them. But the dinosaur bones didn't just get up and walk there. They had to be dug out of the ground, slowly and with great care.

Even today, digging up dinosaurs is not easy. A team of scientists work together.

This is how they do it. First, they have to find a dinosaur. They search along rivers and in quarries. They climb up high rocks and down into deep canyons.

CORYTHOSAURUS
(DUCK BILL DINOSAUR)
PLANT-EATER

With luck, someone finds a fossil bone showing out of the rock, and the work begins.

Sometimes the fossil is buried so deep, the rock around it has to be cut out.

Dinosaurs have been found in quarries, where rock is cut for use in buildings and roads.

ORNITHOMIMUS

Scientists chip at the rock close to the fossil. They brush away the dirt. As soon as a bone is dug out, it is brushed with shellac. The shellac helps hold the bone together, so it won't fall apart.

Sometimes a skeleton has to be cut apart so that it can be moved. The scientist draws each bone in position. That way, there can be no mix-up later, when someone tries to put the skeleton together.

When the bones are ready to be moved, they are carefully wrapped. Small bones are wrapped in tissue paper, and put into boxes or sacks. Large bones are left half-buried in rock. They will be dug out later, in the museum. These fossils are put in a plaster cast before they are packed. The crates of bones are then ready to be sent to the museum.

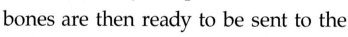

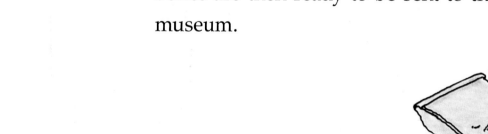

Figuring out how they go together is some job!

At the museum, scientists take out the fossils. They dig the rest of the large bones out of the rock. They study the bones. They compare the bones to other dinosaur bones. They compare them to the bones of other animals. They try to find out how big the dinosaur was and what it looked like. They try to find out how the dinosaur stood and walked, and what it ate.

APATOSAURUS (BRONTOSAURUS)
PLANT-EATER

This rock is 115 million years old. That means the dinosaur is, too.

I can tell from these many flat teeth that this was a plant-eater.

Scientists dig out the fossil in many different ways. They use a hammer and chisel, fine needles, power tools like a dentist's drill, special sandblasting machines, or even chemicals that dissolve the rock but do not harm the fossil.

161

If there are many bones, scientists are able to build a skeleton. The bones are put together, one by one. They are held in place with pieces of metal. If any bones are missing, fiberglass ones are made instead. It is hard to tell the new bones from the old.

After many months the work is done. The dinosaur skeleton looks just as it once did.

Until a while ago only a few museums had dinosaurs. Then scientists found a way to make copies of the skeletons.

The copy is hard to make. It takes a long time. The real skeleton has to be taken apart, bone by bone. A mold is made for each bone. The new pieces are made of fiberglass. A fiberglass dinosaur is just as scary as the real dinosaur skeleton, but much stronger and lighter.

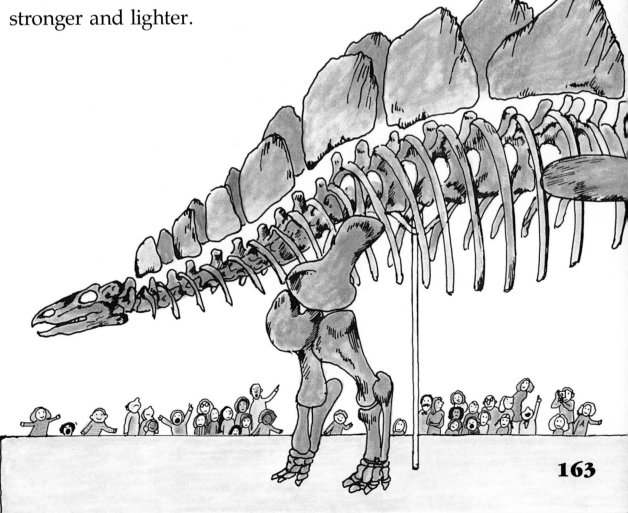

Now museums all over the world have dinosaur skeletons. And many people can spend time looking at them, the way I do.

See you in the museum sometime!

A Reader Says

I would like to become a scientist who studies dinosaurs when I grow up.

How did you feel about the story?

After You Read

Thinking About What You Read

1. What is so special about dinosaurs?

2. Why do scientists take care to draw the dinosaur bones?

3. Why would a museum want a copy of a dinosaur skeleton?

4. How can fossils and skeletons tell us more about these creatures?

Thinking About How You Read

How did asking yourself what the story is about help you understand it?

Sharing and Listening

Tell if you think we will ever find out why dinosaurs became extinct. Why or why not? Listen as others give their ideas.

Writing

Pretend that you are looking for fossils. Write a few sentences telling what kind of work you have to do to dig up dinosaur bones.

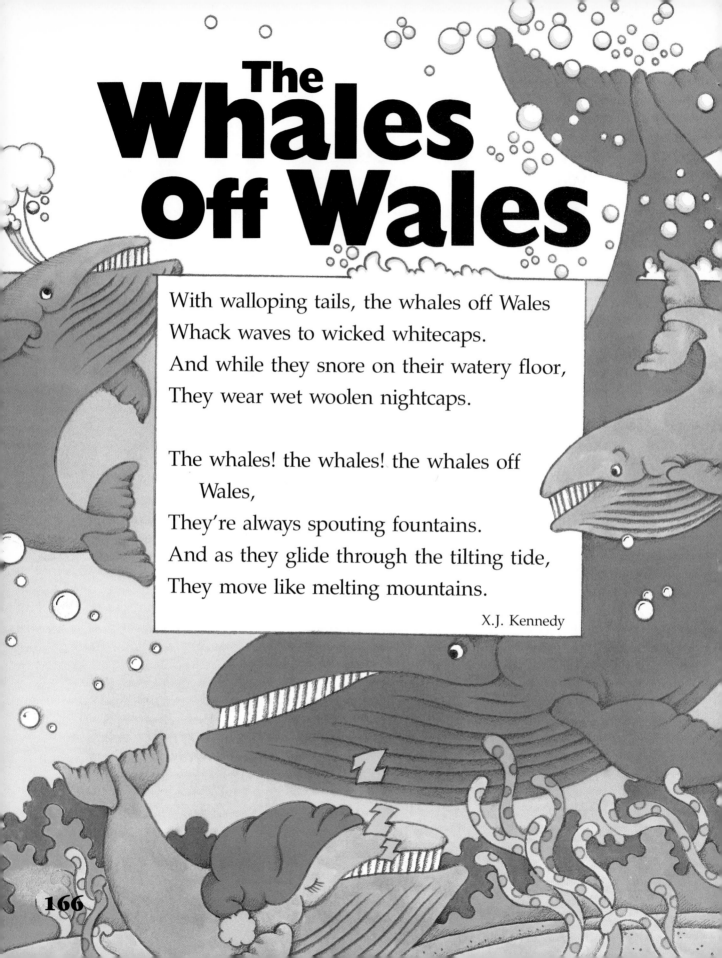

The Whales Off Wales

With walloping tails, the whales off Wales
Whack waves to wicked whitecaps.
And while they snore on their watery floor,
They wear wet woolen nightcaps.

The whales! the whales! the whales off
   Wales,
They're always spouting fountains.
And as they glide through the tilting tide,
They move like melting mountains.

X.J. Kennedy

Understanding Fables

Starting with What You Know

Some stories have animals that act like people. What stories like this do you know?

Thinking About Fables

A **fable** is a kind of story. Some fables that are told today were made up long, long ago. Most fables have animals and people in them. The animals often act like people. In most fables, the animals or people face a problem. When the problem is solved, the animals or people learn a lesson. When you read a fable, you learn the lesson too. Most of the lessons in fables are about how people should behave.

As You Read

As you read the fables that follow, ask yourself this question. "What lessons does this fable teach me?" Use the notes in blue to help you.

167

Long ago, Aesop wrote fables about many different creatures. Read on to find out which of the creatures in the next two fables are great and which are less than great.

Aesop's Fables

The Lion and the Mouse

A lion was sleeping under a tree. A mouse, not looking where he was going, ran over the nose of the mighty lion and woke him up.

The lion put his paw on top of the scared little creature and was about to make an end of him. The mouse, in a mild little voice, said, "Please, do not hurt me. I lost my way and was scared. I never meant to hurt you. If you will let me go, I will always be your friend. Maybe someday I can pay you back by doing something for you."

The mouse talks and acts like a person.

"Pay me back! What an idea!" laughed the mighty lion. For he thought that a creature so small could never help him. But he let the mouse go.

The lion acts like a person, too.

Now it happened soon after that the lion, while walking in the woods, fell into a trap set for him. Finding himself trapped in the ropes with no hope of getting free, he let out a roar that filled the forest with its sound.

The lion has a problem. Think about what will happen next.

169

The mouse, knowing that the roar was the voice of the lion who had set him free, ran to the spot. He set to work to nibble the ropes that held the lion.

His teeth were sharp, and so it was not long before he nibbled through the ropes and the mighty lion was once again free. The lion was wiser now, knowing that a kindness is never wasted, for there is no creature too small to pay back a kindness.

An act of kindness is never wasted.

This is what the lion learns.

170

The Greedy Dog

One day a greedy dog stole a piece of
meat from a meat shop. The dog had to walk
over a bridge to get home. When he got on
the bridge, he looked into the water. He saw
a dog holding a piece of meat in his teeth.
He did not know that he was seeing himself
on the water.

171

Notice that the dog thinks out his plan like a person.

The dog acts like a person and learns a lesson.

The greedy dog thought to himself that he would take the piece of meat from the other dog. Then he would have two pieces. But when he opened his mouth to grab the other piece of meat, the piece of meat in his own mouth fell into the river.

The greedy dog was left with nothing.

One who is greedy may end up with nothing.

A Reader Says

I felt bad for the dog. He didn't know it was himself he was seeing in the water. He was just very hungry.

How did you feel about the stories?

172

After You Read

Thinking About What You Read

1. Why did the lion let the mouse go?

2. What might have happened to the lion if the mouse hadn't been a true friend?

3. How did the mouse show that even an animal as great as a lion needs to have friends?

4. How did the dog show that he was greedy and not just hungry?

Thinking About How You Read

How did knowing that the animals are meant to be like people help you understand the characters?

Sharing and Listening

Tell which of the animals in the two fables you thought was the greatest or the kindest. Why? Listen as other people give their ideas.

Writing

Write a story about how a small animal might help a big animal.

To mice, a cat can seem a great, big, scary creature. In this play based on a fable by Aesop, some mice want to save their town from a cat. What can they do?

Belling the Cat

by Laura Schenone

CAST

AESOP	RANDOLPH
JOAN	CHARLES
THE MAYOR	JENNY
BERNARD	BETH

AESOP: Once there was a small town where many mice made their home. It was a very nice town for mice. There were schools and stores and a baseball team. There was even a mayor to help the mice run the town. One morning the mayor wakes up to the sound of knocking. She runs to see who it is.

MAYOR: Who in the world could be in such a hurry to see me? Joan! What has happened?

JOAN: The Cat just chased me clear across the field. I was nibbling on some nuts when I saw The Cat. Mayor, you have to do something. It's impossible to be safe from The Cat!

MAYOR: (*sighing*) I know. I just had a close call myself. The other day I was walking to the City Hole and The Cat came out of nowhere. I had to dive under some leaves.

JOAN: Mayor, this can't go on. We are all living in fear. The Cat is everywhere, and it's your job to do something!

MAYOR: Tell all the mice to come to the Town Meeting Hole tonight. We'll take care of this cat once and for all.

176

AESOP: The news travels fast.
Every mouse is at the Town
Meeting Hole that night. All of them
are talking at once. The air buzzes with
stories of close calls with The Cat.

MAYOR: Friends, I will not waste your time
with a long speech. We are here to
talk about a big problem. Tonight, we
must face the thing that makes us live
in fear. We must do something about
our number one problem . . . The Cat.

ALL OF THE MICE: Boo! Hiss! Boo!

CHARLES: It's easy to boo. The hard part is
to think of what to do.

MAYOR: Charles is right! We need a plan.
Does anyone have an idea to suggest?

BERNARD: I do! I suggest we move!

ALL OF THE MICE: Move??!!

BERNARD: Yes, move. The Cat never leaves this field. I know a pretty spot where The Cat never goes. There is a flower bed at the end of the field.

JENNY: Where is this place?

BERNARD: It is on the other side of the wall.

MAYOR: How do you get there?

BERNARD: Go to the big hole under the wall. Turn right. Follow the old road for fifty feet to a large field. Turn left when you see a piece of paper that reads "WATCH OUT—MOUSETRAP AHEAD." Keep walking. At the end of the field is a nice pond. We could build a new town next to the pond. Then we would be safe.

CHARLES: What, Bernard? Run? That doesn't sound like fun. *This* is the best field around. We must stay here and stand our ground!

MAYOR: Charles is right again. We need a better plan.

JENNY: (*whispering*) Maybe we're too noisy. If we can be more quiet, then The Cat will not be able to find us. We will never have to run from him again.

CHARLES: Jenny, your plan is very nice, but we are already as quiet as mice. The Cat is so sly, he never says meow. He may even be listening to us now! (*All the mice in the Town Meeting Hole look around them in fear of The Cat.*)

ALL OF THE MICE: Oh what will we do!

RANDOLPH: I have it! I know what we might do. We can meet with The Cat and talk things over. Maybe we could get him to see our side. Maybe we could get him to leave us alone.

CHARLES: Randolph, that's a very nice wish, but we might as well jump into The Cat's food dish. We can no longer pretend that The Cat is our friend.

MAYOR: (*sighing*) Once again you're right, Charles. Talking to The Cat would be impossible. But there must be something we can do. Doesn't anyone else have an idea?

CHARLES: Well, mayor, I do. Let me tell it to you.

AESOP: All of the mice get very quiet so they can hear every word.

CHARLES: Mayor, The Cat always finds us because he is so sly and quiet. I have a plan and I think we might try it. We need something, it is clear, that will let us know when he is near. If The Cat would make noise, he would never find us. We could all run away when we heard him behind us. Let's get a bell and a little bit of string. We will put it around his neck and be able to hear it ring.

AESOP: The mice cheer and clap. They are very happy. It is the best idea they have ever heard. Soon they can be rid of The Cat. Then, Beth, the oldest, smartest mouse of all stands up and speaks in a mild voice.

181

BETH: I like that idea, Charles. Now I know why all the mice look up to you. But I have just one thing to ask. I think you know what I'm getting at. . . . Who will be the mouse to put the bell on The Cat?

AESOP: It is easy to suggest impossible solutions.

A Reader Says

I thought Bernard's idea was the best. All the mice could move and build a new town. Then they'd be safe.

How did you feel about the play?

After You Read

Thinking About What You Read

1. What is special about the mice in this play?

2. Why were so many mice afraid of one cat?

3. What might have happened if the mice had tried to carry out Bernard's plan?

4. How might Charles have answered if another mouse had suggested putting a bell on the cat?

Thinking About How You Read

How did knowing the mice would learn something help you understand the ending of the fable?

Sharing and Listening

Think about the mice in this play and the mouse in *The Lion and the Mouse*. Compare their problems. Tell how they are the same or different. Listen as other people share their ideas.

Writing

Pretend you are a mouse. Write a story about how the cat scared you. Tell how you would make the cat leave.

Veronica the hippopotamus wants to be different. But how can she when everyone looks just like her? Find out what happens when Veronica leaves her home and goes to a place where she *can* be different.

Veronica

by Roger Duvoisin

A hippopotamus can sometimes be very conspicuous.

But not so Veronica. She was a most inconspicuous hippopotamus because she lived with so many mother and father hippopotamuses, uncle and aunt hippopotamuses, brother and sister hippopotamuses, and cousin hippopotamuses that no one ever knew Veronica was there.

"No one notices me," she sighed unhappily. "I don't even know myself."

Not even sleeping on the cool mud of the river bank or swimming and splashing in the river could make Veronica happy.

"Oh," she sighed, "I want to be different. In fact, I would like very much to be *famous*."

So Veronica walked away by herself, one day, to find a country where she could be different . . . or even famous. She walked for days, eating grass and leaves along the way.

One afternoon from the top of a hill she saw a pink and white city. The streets were crowded with men and women—even more crowded than Veronica's hippopotamus river.

When Veronica reached the streets of the city, she *knew* she was different. THERE WASN'T ANOTHER HIPPOPOTAMUS IN SIGHT!

There were only people, and they stared at Veronica, bumped into her, and shouted at her when she stepped on their toes.

Veronica was very conspicuous!

Veronica tried to walk in the middle of the street where there were no people. *But* cars bumped into her, and horns blew angrily. Even the police officer blew his whistle.

"Lady," he said, "this is a one-way street, and you are going the wrong way."

Veronica turned around and followed the traffic. She felt very tired and sleepy and looked around for a place to rest.

There was no soft mud bank, but Veronica thought the sidewalk looked cool. She stretched out and went to sleep, to dream happily of being a conspicuous hippopotamus . . . perhaps even a famous hippopotamus.

Now, Veronica was not only conspicuous,
she was very much in the way, and was told
to move on. She obliged politely, but with a
sigh, for she was very tired. She went to lie
down at the curb. It would do just as well as
the sidewalk.

The police officer, though, did not think
so. "Lady," he said, "you can't park here."
But this time he showed her a place across
the street where she could sleep quietly.

187

"I don't know how these people can sleep without a soft mud bank," Veronica thought as she crossed the street. "Still, it is very quiet, and maybe I can sleep here."

Even in her sleep Veronica was now so conspicuous that people gathered to look at her.

Now, even a conspicuous hippopotamus must have food to eat, and water to drink and to splash in, and mud to wallow in.

The next morning, Veronica started out to search for these things.

Soon, she found a fountain with little goldfish swimming round and round.

"No people in the water?" wondered Veronica. "It must be that people do not drink water or take baths."

But Veronica waded into the fountain happily. She drank, she splashed, and she rolled on her back in the cool water.

Out splashed the water all over the people on the sidewalk, and soon the fountain was empty.

Veronica did not notice that people were angry with her now. She smiled with joy at the sight of a man who was walking by, pushing a cart of fresh vegetables.

Not used to city manners, Veronica helped herself happily to the fresh food. In one gulp, she emptied the cart clean.

"Help!" shouted the man.

"What happened here?" shouted a police officer, hearing all the noise.

"She stole my vegetables," cried the man, "and she ate them all in one gulp."

"What!" said the officer. "In one gulp?"

"One gulp! Look at her mouth."

"Well then," said the police officer to
Veronica, "you are under arrest. You step on
people's feet; you stop the traffic; you bathe
in the fountain, and now you steal. Come
along to jail!"

Veronica did not know what a jail was,
but the police officer's loud voice so scared
her that she ran down the street looking for
a place to hide. Everyone ran after her.

At the end of the street she saw a park.

"I'm saved," she thought. "I'll hide behind
a bench and escape from this city when
it's dark."

But even behind a bench, Veronica was
still conspicuous.

She soon found herself with a rope around
her neck and on her way to jail.

If Veronica had never seen a jail, the jail
had never seen a hippopotamus. It had NOT
been made for hippopotamuses. The door
was too narrow for Veronica.

She couldn't go through it even with
people pushing from behind and pulling
from in front.

Finally, a bulldozer was brought to help push Veronica through the narrow door. With one push she was *in* the jail.

At that moment, a nice lady came in and said, "Aren't you ashamed to do this to a poor hippopotamus?"

"Well," said the police officer, "she ate all of this poor man's vegetables."

"Yes, all of *my* vegetables," said the man.

The lady opened her bag, gave the man some money, and asked, "Does this repay you for your vegetables?"

"Oh, yes," he said, "and I thank you."

"Well then," said the lady, "let this hippopotamus out at once."

"I can't," said the police officer, "because the door is too narrow and the bulldozer can't come in to push her out from behind."

"Then tear down the door," ordered the nice lady. The door was torn down. Veronica was free!

The nice lady also seemed to know that Veronica had had enough of the city, and that she was tired of being conspicuous.

One can be *too* conspicuous.

"I only want to go home to my mud bank," said Veronica, "to my river, to all my hippopotamuses."

The lady ordered a moving van to move Veronica back to her country. And that was done too.

Veronica left the city as the police officer, the vegetable seller, the nice lady, and all the people cheered her.

So, that was how Veronica wallowed again in the cool mud by the river bank, and swam and splashed in the clear river water with all the father, mother, brother, sister, aunt, uncle, and cousin hippopotamuses.

But there was a difference.

She was now famous among
hippopotamuses and beloved by all of them.
Almost everyday at sunset they gathered
around her to hear about her marvelous
adventures in the pink and white city.

And Veronica was very happy.

A Reader Says

*I think Veronica should try visiting the city
again. This time she might bring another
hippopotamus with her.*

How did you feel about the story?

About the Author

Roger Duvoisin

Roger Duvoisin was born in Switzerland. When he was little, he loved to draw and listen to animal stories.

When he came to live in the United States, he began writing and drawing books for children. Some of his books are *Veronica and the Birthday Present*; *Petunia, I Love You*; and *Petunia, the Silly Goose Stories*. Mr. Duvoisin not only drew his own books, he also drew for books by many other authors.

Mr. Duvoisin died in 1980. He was 76 years old.

More Books About Great Creatures

The Story of Babar
by Jean de Brunhoff

You'll meet Babar, the king of the elephants, in this book, and find out that he likes wearing round black hats and green coats, and likes to go to sleep in his bed after eating. You'll also read about the many things that happen to him.

Blizzard at the Zoo
by Robert Bahr

A zoo is a nice place to visit when the weather is warm. But what happens to the animals in the winter? This book tells the true story of what happens when a bad snow storm hits a zoo one winter.

Once in a Wood: Ten Tales from Aesop
by Eve Rice

If you liked the three fables that you read, you'll want to read more fables in this book.

MAKING ALL THE
CONNECTIONS
Speaking and Listening

In this part of the book, you read stories about great creatures. You read how a little gorilla learned that everyone would still love him when he was big. You read how some great creatures talk to each other. You read about how we know about the dinosaurs. You even read about a hippopotamus who wanted to see the city!

Talk to your classmates about the great creatures you read about. You may want to look at your Reader's Log. Speak slowly and in a clear voice. Listen when the other children in your class talk.

Think about this before you begin. Not all great creatures are alike. Some live in water, while others live on land. Still others lived long ago and then died out. Some are great in size. Some show their greatness in other ways. What is it about different creatures that makes them great?

Thinking About Pictures

In this part of the book, you met a lot of great creatures. Thinking about them is one way of remembering them. Another way is to draw or cut out pictures of them. If everyone made pictures of nine great creatures, do you think everyone would choose the same creatures? Do you think that the pictures would look alike? Let's find out.

Work with a partner. Think of nine great creatures and make a list of them. You can choose creatures that you read about in this part of the book, or think of your own. Think about how the great creatures that you pick are alike or different. Look at the great-creatures picture on this page. The nine great creatures are arranged across and down. Think about how you could arrange your creatures in a picture.

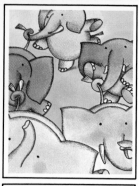

Making a Picture

Work with a partner. You will need a big piece of paper, nine small pieces of paper, crayons, old magazines, scissors, and glue. You can draw your great creatures, or cut them out of magazines.

1. On the small pieces of paper, draw or paste the pictures of the creatures you and your partner picked.

2. Think about how you want to arrange the pictures on the big piece of paper. You can arrange them in the order that you thought of them. You can arrange the pictures by how the creatures are alike or different. You can arrange the pictures your own way. Try more than one way.

3. Glue the pictures on to your big piece of paper.

Sharing Your Picture

You and your friend have made a great-creatures picture. Now, you can share your picture with the rest of the class. You can see what great creatures were chosen by the other children in your class. You can see what great-creature pictures look alike. Here are some ways you can show your picture and see everyone else's.

Talk About Your Picture

Show your picture to the class. Tell the name of each creature and what you like about it. Then tell why you and your partner picked each great creature. You can also tell why you arranged the pictures the way you did. Then, look at the pictures the other children in your class made. Listen while they talk.

Make a Great Creature Mural

Paste all of the pictures on a long piece of paper. Hang up your mural in the classroom. You can even hang it in the school library for everyone to share.

PART FOUR

Small Creatures

Little snail,
Dreaming as you go.
Weather and rose
Is all you know.

from *Snail*
by Langston Hughes

—————◆—————

The world is filled with small creatures.
Some are so small that it's hard to see them.
To learn about small creatures, you need
only to open your eyes and look around you.
As you read, think: What will you see when
you turn the page?

Using Words About Small Creatures

Starting with What You Know

Think about small creatures. What ideas can you come up with? The words in the box tell about small creatures. Use these words and other words you know to answer the questions after the box.

mouse	little	nest
furry	ant	tree
bird	grass	quick

What is a kind of small creature? How would you describe a small creature? Where are places a small creature might live?

Words can be fun.

Building a Word Map

The word map shows how some of the words in the box above go together. Think about words you can put on the map.

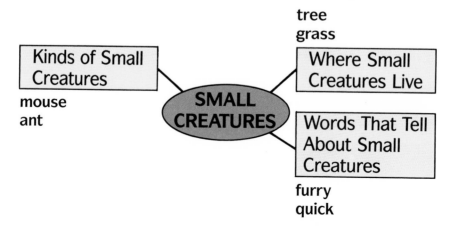

tree
grass

Kinds of Small Creatures

mouse
ant

SMALL CREATURES

Where Small Creatures Live

Words That Tell About Small Creatures

furry
quick

Finishing a Story

Look at the story below. The story tells about a small creature. Some words are left out. Think of the words you would use to finish the story. Use the words from the box and word map in this lesson for ideas. Complete the story.

Addy was a _____ mouse. Addy lived alone in a _____. One day, Addy was taking a walk. She saw a _____ cat. She ran into her _____ house.

"Come out," said the cat. "I will invite you to lunch."

"I will eat my _____." said Addy. "I do not want to be your lunch!"

Share your story with your class. What words did the children in your class use?

As You Read

In this part of the book, you will read about small creatures. Keep a Reader's Log. A Reader's Log will help you remember thoughts, ideas, and new words. Start the log with the word map. Write new words on your map as you find them.

Is a person *really* a person no matter how small? That's what Horton the elephant thinks. He finds out he's right when he hears a faint call coming from a speck of dust.

HORTON HEARS A WHO!

◆

by Dr. Seuss

". . . I say!" murmured Horton. "I've never heard tell
Of a small speck of dust that is able to yell.
So you know what I think? . . . Why, I think that there must
Be someone on top of that small speck of dust!
Some sort of a creature of very small size,
Too small to be seen by an elephant's eyes. . . .

". . . some poor little person who's shaking
with fear
That he'll blow in the pool! He has no way
to steer!
I'll just have to save him. Because, after all,
A person's a person, no matter how small."
. . . The voice was so faint he could just
barely hear it.
"Speak *up*, please," said Horton. He put his
ear near it.
"My friend," came the voice, "you're a *very*
fine friend.
You've helped all us folks on this dust
speck no end.
You've saved all our houses, our ceilings
and floors.
You've saved all our churches and grocery
stores."

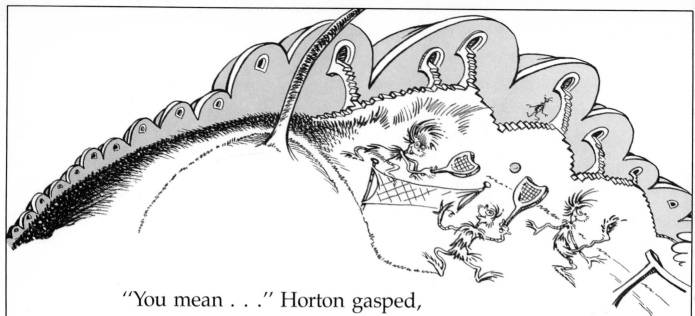

"You mean . . ." Horton gasped,
   "you have *buildings* there, *too*?"
"Oh yes," piped the voice. "We most
   certainly do. . . .

. . . My town is called *Who*-ville, for I am a *Who*
And we *Whos* are all thankful and grateful to
   you."
And Horton called back to the Mayor of the
   town,
"You're safe now. Don't worry. I won't
   let you down."

Thinking About the Theme

1. Why does Horton care about creatures
   that are so small?

2. What is the smallest creature you can
   think of? What do you know about it?

Understanding
How to Compare Things

How are the two animals the same? How are they different?

Thinking About Comparing Things

In stories, the writer sometimes compares two things to help you understand them better. The two things may be alike in some ways, but different in others. How are the two dogs the same or different in this story?

Annie had two dogs. Both dogs were small with black spots. One dog had a short tail. The other dog had a long tail.

As You Read

As you read the two stories that follow, ask yourself this question. "How are these things alike and how are they different?" Use the notes in blue to help you.

Ah Kim wants a pet, but the pet she gets
must be small enough to fit in a rice bowl.
What would be the perfect pet?

The Rice Bowl Pet

by Patricia Miles Martin

From the window of her home, Ah Kim
could see her neighbors and their pets.

One day Ah Kim asked her mother, "Will
I ever have a pet like our neighbors do?"

"Our home is small," her mother said. "You may have a small pet. But it must fit in a rice bowl."

Ah Kim looked at her rice bowl. It was very small.

Think about the kind of pet Ah Kim might have.

The next morning Ah Kim said, "I will take my rice bowl with me and find a pet that will fit." She walked up the hill to the main street, where there were many shops. Every shop had things to look at. In one window she saw a small, shiny jade elephant.

"That jade elephant is small enough to fit in my rice bowl," she said. But she wanted a live pet.

Ah Kim compares the size of the elephant to her bowl. It fits, but the elephant is different from a real pet.

She looked in the window and she saw something run across the shop. It was a little dog, the smallest dog she had ever seen. It jumped into a basket.

211

The dog would make a nice pet, but it would not fit in the rice bowl.

Ah Kim pressed her face on the window and the little dog raised its eyes and looked back at her.

The shopkeeper came outside. "Do not press your face on my window," he said. "People come to look at the dog in my shop, and I must always wash the marks from this window after they go."

Ah Kim walked on to the pet shop. There she saw some fish and frogs. But she wanted a warm pet. She could not forget about the little dog.

On her way home, she stopped at the shop with the shiny jade elephant in the window. The little dog was still there. Ah Kim pressed her face to the window.

The shopkeeper came outside. "You again," he said. "You come to look in my window so I have to wash away the marks again. Please go."

"I will wash the window for you," Ah Kim said.

"But you did not make all the marks," the shopkeeper said.

"I know," said Ah Kim, "but I made many of them. I would like to wash the window."

"Very good," said the man.

Ah Kim made the window shiny and bright again.

Think about what will happen next.

Then the shopkeeper called, "Come in, come in. My brother is taking the little dog away soon, but he will not take one puppy." He reached inside the basket. In his raised hand was the smallest puppy she had ever seen. It was the perfect size.

The shopkeeper said, "If you will take this puppy, then people will not press their faces on our window."

The puppy is the right size.

Ah Kim found what she wanted. Now she is happy.

The puppy was warm and it was small enough to fit into her rice bowl.

Ah Kim wanted to thank the man, but no words would come to say thank you.

The shopkeeper's wife smiled. "You do not have to speak any words to thank us," she said. "Words could not say the thanks we see on your face."

Ah Kim left the main street, holding the puppy in her rice bowl. She walked down the hill and up the steps to her home.

"Look," she said. "I found a pet that will fit in my rice bowl!"

Her brothers laughed, and her mother laughed too.

And Ah Kim laughed the most of all.

A Reader Says

Puppies are cute! I hope Ah Kim's mother lets her keep the dog even if it gets much bigger.

How did you feel about the story?

After You Read

Thinking About What You Read

1. What kind of pet did Ah Kim really want? Why do you think so?

2. Why did Ah Kim go back to the window after the man told her to go away?

3. How did the man feel about Ah Kim? Why did he give her a puppy?

4. Why did everybody laugh when Ah Kim brought her pet home?

Thinking About How You Read

How did knowing how to compare things help you think about the pets?

Sharing and Listening

Do you think that Ah Kim's mother will let her keep her pet? Why or why not? Listen as others give their ideas.

Writing

Name some animals that would fit into a rice bowl and stay small. Then name some animals that might fit when they were small but not once they grew bigger.

Some small creatures make good pets. But what happens when a small bird decides to make a pet out of a person?

Janey's Boss

by Lilian Moore

Boss was a crow, a big black crow. He was Janey Fisher's pet.

Where did Boss come from?

"Out of the sky," said Janey. That was true.

One day the big black crow flew out of the sky into the yard. He flew down into the big old peach tree. He looked around. And he decided to stay.

Sometimes people said, "Janey, is that crow your pet?"

Then Janey said, "Yes, but he thinks I am *his* pet."

That was true, too.

Janey did not choose the crow. The crow chose Janey. One morning he flew right into Janey's room. He sat on the bed beside Janey and looked at her. Then he flew up and sat on her head.

"See!" said Janey's mother, laughing. "You are the girl for him!"

Janey *was* the girl for Boss. The crow wanted to be with Janey all the time. It was funny to see him walking beside her. Sometimes he looked at Janey as if to say, "Why don't we fly, silly girl? Oh, well, if you walk, I will walk, too."

Janey gave the crow his name. Boss was his name, and bossy he was. That crow did just what he wanted to do.

Did Boss feel hungry? He took what he wanted.

Once the crow flew off with Dad's lunch. How angry Janey's father was! "You old bird!" he yelled up at the crow.

Did Boss feel like playing? He took the toys he wanted.

One day Janey's brother Dick was working on a puzzle. The crow flew down beside the table. He upset the puzzle and flew off with a piece of it.

How angry Dick was!

"Now I can't do my puzzle!" Dick said.

"Oh, no," Janey told her crow. "It seems that only Mother and I like you any more!"

Janey's mother did like Boss—most of the time. Then one day she hung out a line full of white clothes. Boss flew down and pulled off all the clothespins. Every last one!

After that, Janey decided to have a talk with her bossy crow.

"Look here, Boss," she said. "I am going to teach you something. When I say STOP THAT, you must do what I say!"

Janey went around saying STOP THAT to Boss. Boss did learn. But what did he learn?

He learned to say STOP THAT! He loved to
say it out loud again and again.

One morning the milkman was putting the
Fisher's milk in front of the house.

"STOP THAT!" someone said.

The milkman jumped back to the curb. He
looked around, but saw no one. So he put
the milk back.

"STOP THAT!" someone said.

The milkman jumped back to the curb again. Again he looked around and saw no one. Again he put the milk down. Again he heard, "STOP THAT!"

This time the milkman looked up and saw Boss. How angry the milkman was!

"Oh, Boss!" scolded Janey. "Everybody is so angry with you. What is the matter with you?"

Boss flew to Janey and sat on her head.

"STOP THAT!" said Boss. And Janey had to laugh.

Then one day something happened. After that no one was angry with Janey's pet any more.

Boss was up in the peach tree. He looked down and saw something.

"STOP THAT!" he cried. "STOP THAT!" out loud—again and again. "STOP THAT! STOP THAT! STOP THAT!"

Janey's mother came out of the house to scold him. Then she saw what Boss saw. The neighbor's baby was walking out into the road!

Mr. Fisher ran out and got him—fast!

What a fuss everyone made about Boss.

They made such a fuss that he yelled, "STOP THAT!"

Where had Boss come from? Out of the sky—just like that. One day—just like that—Boss was gone. Some wild crows flew over the old peach tree. Boss saw them, and off he went—back into the sky.

It was a sad day for Janey.

"He was the best pet I ever had," she said.

"I know how you feel," said her mother. "I miss that old Boss, too."

That made Janey feel a little better.

"I miss the old bird, too," her father said one night.

"So do I," said Dick.

That made Janey feel much better.

"Do you think Boss will come back someday?" she asked.

"Maybe," said her father. "If he wants my lunch."

"Maybe," said Dick. "If he misses my toys."

"Most of all," said Janey's mother, "Boss will come back when he misses his girl."

"When will that be?" Janey wanted to know.

"He'll come back any time he wants to," said Janey's mother. "After all, he's the Boss!"

A Reader Says

I think Boss was as smart as a person!

How did you feel about the story?

After You Read

Thinking About What You Read

1. How did Boss get along with Janey and her family?

2. In what way did Janey's plan to teach Boss work? In what way did it not work?

3. Why did Boss fly off with the wild crows?

4. Why did Janey's family miss Boss after he flew away?

Thinking About How You Read

How did comparing Boss to other pets you know help you understand the story?

Sharing and Listening

Tell if you think a crow would be a good pet. What do you think would be fun about having Boss for a pet? What would be hard? Listen as others give their ideas.

Writing

Write a short story about why Boss comes back or does not come back.

A STOP SIGN for BIRDS

In the story *Janey's Boss*, Janey has a bird for a friend. You, too, can be a friend to birds by warning them of dangers.

A bird can be hurt by flying into a window. It may think the window is an open space. Or, the bird may look in the glass and think it is seeing a different bird. Thinking to chase others away, a bird may dive into the window. Often, the bird breaks its neck.

If birds sometimes fly near the windows of your house or school, you can help warn them with a window "stop sign." It is easy to make, and could save a bird's life.

First, take a large piece of dark paper and fold it in half. Then, draw half an outline of an eagle or other large bird that smaller birds would want to stay away from. Cut out the drawing, open it, and tape it to a window. Birds will be sure to stay away from this "stop sign."

Understanding Poems

STRATEGY ◀BUILDER▶

for **Bug Poems** and **Cat and Mouse Poems**

Starting with What You Know

Poems are sets of words that seem like songs. They can be easy to remember, and fun to say out loud. What poems do you remember?

Thinking About Poems

A poem can be about anything. Some poems tell a story. Some poems tell about feelings. A poem can tell about what it is like to feel happy. A poem can also be about feeling sad. Poems often have words that sound the same, such as *moon* and *soon*. A poem paints a picture with words. The poem can help you see something in a new way or it can make you feel a special way.

As You Read

As you read the poems that follow, ask yourself this question. "What does this poem help me see or feel?" Use the notes in blue to help you.

You can write a poem about anything—even a creature as small as a bug. You may think about bugs in a new way after you read the poems that follow.

Bug Poems

I Like BUGS

You can tell what this poem is about.

Bug and *rug* are words that sound alike. You can find two more.

Think about how this poem makes you feel.

I like bugs
Black bugs Green bugs
Bad bugs Mean bugs
Any kind of a bug
A bug in a rug
A bug in the grass
A bug on the sidewalk
A bug in a glass
I like bugs
Round bugs Shiny bugs
Fat bugs Buggy bugs
Big bugs Lady bugs
I like bugs.

Margaret Wise Brown

227

Little Talk

Think about how
bugs might talk.

Don't you think it's probable
that beetles, bugs, and bees
talk about a lot of things—
you know, such things as these:

Grass and *pass*
are words that
sound alike. You
can find more.

The kind of weather where they live
in jungles tall with grass
and earthquakes in their villages
whenever people pass!

Of course, we'll never know if bugs
talk very much at all,
because our ears are far too big
for talk that is so small.

Aileen Fisher

A Reader Says

*I like looking at bugs. I'd like to learn more about
different kinds of bugs.*

How did you feel about the poems?

228

After You Read

Thinking About What You Read

1. Why did the person who wrote "I Like Bugs" write this poem?

2. What makes "I Like Bugs" funny? Why is this poem nice to read out loud?

3. What does the person who wrote "Little Talk" like to think about bugs?

4. How does "Little Talk" compare the sizes of people and bugs?

Thinking About How You Read

How did knowing that poems are different from stories help you read?

Sharing and Listening

Tell if you like to read poems about small creatures, such as bugs. Why or why not? Listen as other people give their ideas.

Writing

Write a short poem or story about bugs or how you feel about bugs.

Poets often write about animals. Here four poets give their ideas about cats and mice.

Cat and Mouse Poems

Cats

Cats sleep
Anywhere,
Any table,
Any chair,
Top of piano,
Window-ledge,
In the middle,
On the edge,
Open drawer,
Empty shoe,

Anybody's
Lap will do,
Fitted in a
Cardboard box,
In the cupboard
With your frocks—
Anywhere!
They don't care!
Cats sleep
Anywhere.

Eleanor Farjeon

231

Cat

The black cat yawns,
Opens her jaws,
Stretches her legs,
And shows her claws.

Then she gets up
And stands on four
Long stiff legs
And yawns some more.

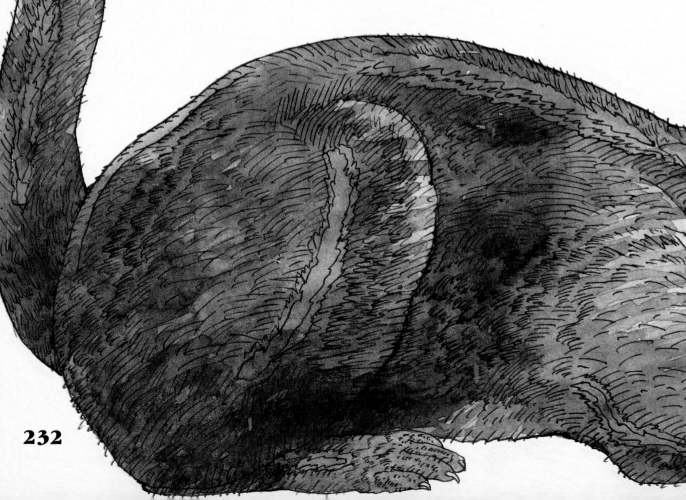

She shows her sharp teeth,
She stretches her lip,
Her slice of a tongue
Turns up at the tip.

Lifting herself
On her delicate toes,
She arches her back
As high as it goes.

She lets herself down
With particular care,
And pads away
With her tail in the air.

Mary Britton Miller

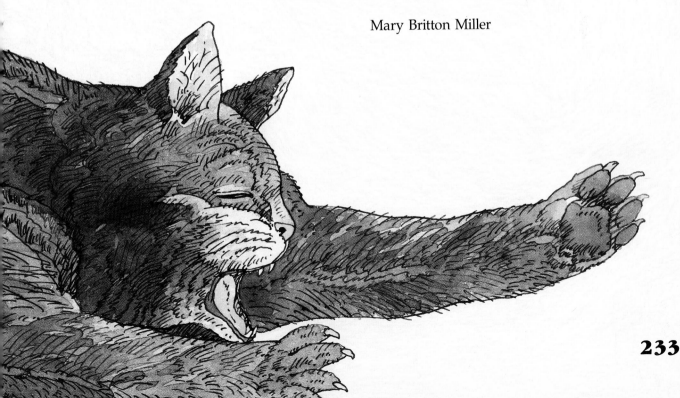

Mice

I think mice
Are rather nice.

Their tails are long,
Their faces small,
They haven't any
Chins at all.

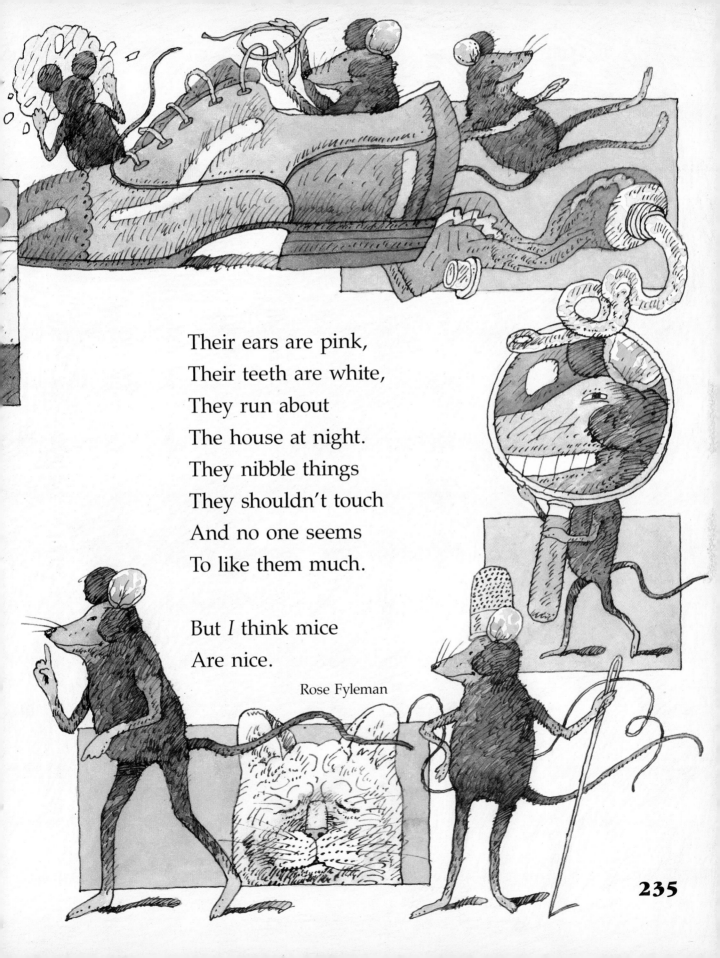

Their ears are pink,
Their teeth are white,
They run about
The house at night.
They nibble things
They shouldn't touch
And no one seems
To like them much.

But *I* think mice
Are nice.

Rose Fyleman

235

The Old Woman

You know the old woman
    Who lived in a shoe?
And had so many children
    She didn't know what to do?

I think if she lived in
    A little shoe-house—
That little old woman was
    Surely a mouse!

Beatrix Potter

A Reader Says

*I like reading poems about cats and mice. Maybe
I'll write one!*

How did you feel about the poems?

236

After You Read

Thinking About What You Read

1. Why do you think that cats sleep anywhere?

2. The poem "Cat" calls the cat's tongue "a slice." What does that make you think of?

3. Do you think that mice are nice? Tell why or why not.

4. Why does the poet think that the old woman who lived in a shoe is really a mouse?

Thinking About How You Read

How did knowing about poems and rhymes help you understand these poems?

Sharing and Listening

Which poem do you like best? Tell everyone in the class why you like it. Listen as others tell why they like their poems.

Writing

Write your own poem. Copy the line below. Make up another line. If you wish, use these words: *hat sat pat rat fat*.

I have a tiny furry cat.

Alexander, a live mouse, wishes he could be more like his friend Willy, who is a toy mouse. But Alexander learns that sometimes what you wish for isn't what is best.

Alexander and the Wind-up Mouse

by Leo Lionni

"Help! Help! A mouse!" There was a scream. Then a crash. Cups, saucers, and spoons were flying in all directions.

Alexander ran for his hole as fast as his little legs would carry him.

All Alexander wanted was a few crumbs and yet every time they saw him they would scream for help or chase him with a broom.

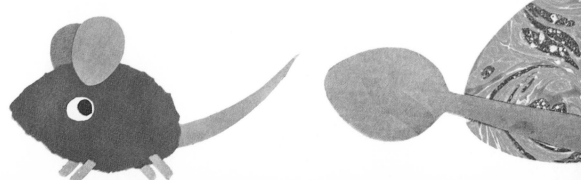

239

One day, when there was no one in the house, Alexander heard a squeak in Annie's room. He sneaked in and what did he see? Another mouse.

But not an ordinary mouse like himself. Instead of legs it had two little wheels, and on its back there was a key.

"Who are you?" asked Alexander.

"I am Willy the wind-up mouse, Annie's favorite toy. They wind me to make me run around in circles, they cuddle me, and at night I sleep on a soft white pillow between the doll and a woolly teddy bear. Everyone loves me."

"They don't care much for me," said Alexander sadly. But he was happy to have found a friend. "Let's go to the kitchen and look for crumbs," he said.

"Oh, I can't," said Willy. "I can only move when they wind me. But I don't mind. Everybody loves me."

Alexander, too, came to love Willy. He
went to visit him whenever he could. He told
him of his adventures with brooms, flying
saucers, and mousetraps. Willy talked about
the penguin, the woolly bear, and mostly
about Annie. The two friends spent many
happy hours together.

But when he was alone in the dark of his hideout, Alexander thought of Willy with envy.

"Ah!" he sighed. "Why can't I be a wind-up mouse like Willy and be cuddled and loved?"

One day Willy told a strange story. "I've heard," he whispered mysteriously, "that in the garden, at the end of the pebblepath, close to the blackberry bush, there lives a magic lizard who can change one animal into another."

"Do you mean," said Alexander, "that he could change me into a wind-up mouse like you?"

That very afternoon Alexander went into the garden and ran to the end of the path. "Lizard, lizard," he whispered. And suddenly there stood before him, full of the colors of flowers and butterflies, a large lizard. "Is it true that you could change me into a wind-up mouse?" asked Alexander in a quivering voice.

"When the moon is round," said the lizard, "bring me a purple pebble."

For days and days Alexander searched the garden for a purple pebble. In vain. He found yellow pebbles and blue pebbles and green pebbles—but not one tiny purple pebble.

At last, tired and hungry, he returned to the house. In a corner of the pantry he saw a box full of old toys, and there, between blocks and broken dolls, was Willy. "What happened?" said Alexander, surprised.

Willy told him a sad story. It had been Annie's birthday. There had been a party and everyone had brought a gift. "The next day," Willy sighed, "many of the old toys were dumped in this box. We will all be thrown away."

Alexander was almost in tears. "Poor, poor Willy!" he thought. But then suddenly something caught his eye. Could it really be . . .? Yes it was! It was a little purple pebble.

All excited, he ran to the garden, the precious pebble tight in his arms. There was a full moon. Out of breath, Alexander stopped near the blackberry bush. "Lizard, lizard, in the bush," he called quickly. The leaves rustled and there stood the lizard. "The moon is round, the pebble found," said the lizard. "Who or what do you wish to be?"

"I want to be . . ." Alexander stopped. Then suddenly he said, "Lizard, lizard, could you change Willy into a mouse like me?" The lizard blinked. There was a blinding light. And then all was quiet. The purple pebble was gone.

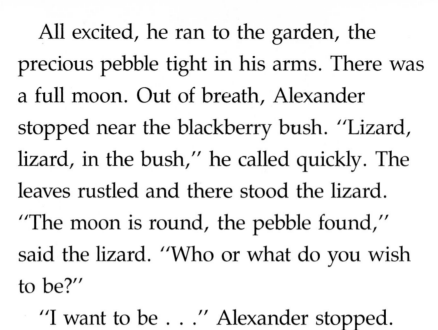

Alexander ran back to the house as fast as he could.

The box was there, but alas it was empty. "Too late," he thought, and with a heavy heart he went to his hole in the baseboard.

Something squeaked! Cautiously
Alexander moved closer to the hole.
There was a mouse inside. "Who
are you?" said Alexander, a little
frightened.

"My name is Willy," said the mouse.

"Willy!" cried Alexander. "The lizard . . . the lizard did it!" He hugged Willy and then they ran to the garden path. And there they danced until dawn.

A Reader Says

I think it's more fun to be real than to be a toy.

How did you feel about the story?

About the Author

Leo Lionni

Leo Lionni was born in Amsterdam, Holland. When he was 29 years old, he came to live in the United States. Before writing books, he painted. His paintings have been shown in museums.

Mr. Lionni does all the drawings for his books. Some of his other books are *The Biggest House in the World*, *Frederick*, and *Geraldine, The Music Mouse*. Mr. Lionni has won many prizes for his books.

Mr. Lionni once said that he wrote for the child in himself who has never grown up. That way, he hopes, the child in every person can enjoy his books.

More Books About Small Creatures

Horton Hatches the Egg

by Dr. Seuss

Can an elephant sit on a tiny egg without it breaking? Can an elephant keep his word to a bird even when the other animals laugh at him? You'll find out when Horton helps a bird hatch an egg.

Out in the Dark and the Daylight

by Aileen Fisher

This book of poems will show you the world of small creatures and other little things that live around us.

The Conversation Club

by Diane Stanley

What do field mice talk about when they get together? Anything and everything, as it turns out. But, as you'll find out, there's more to having a conversation than just talking.

MAKING ALL THE
CONNECTIONS

Speaking and Listening

In this part of the book, you read about some small ceatures. You read about Horton, who thinks that a person's a person no matter how small. You read how Ah Kim tried to find a pet as small as her rice bowl. You read poems about bugs. You read how a small creature called Alexander learned that it was best to be a real mouse.

Think about these stories. Talk about them with your class. You may want to look at your Reader's Log. When you speak, say your words clearly. Listen when the other children in your class talk.

Before you begin, think about this. There are many kinds of small creatures. Some are bugs. Some are birds. Many are other animals. How are the small creatures you read about the same? How are they different? Do you think it would be fun to be a small creature?

Reading Something New About Science

All people like a special place of their own. Here is a story about small creatures who build their own special places.

Chipmunks dig underground tunnels where they live for many years. Beavers build their homes out of sticks and mud. They build them near streams and ponds. A beaver home can last for years and years. Squirrels and raccoons live in hollow logs or dead trees.

Other small creatures live with people. Some fish live in bowls. Some birds live in cages. People also have cats and dogs as pets.

Some bugs build special places where they live together with many other bugs. Ants build tunnels in large mounds of sand. Their homes have lots of ways leading to special rooms. Bees live together in hives made of wax.

Which animal home would you like to visit?

Thinking About Small Creatures

The story you just read told about special places for small creatures. What did you learn about their homes? The stories that you read in this part of your book also told about small creatures. What did the people and animals in each of these stories learn about being small? Tell what you think by finishing the sentences below.

1. I read about small creatures' homes and learned _____.

2. Horton hears a Who and learns _____.

3. Ah Kim wants a small pet and learns _____.

4. Alexander meets another small creature and learns _____.

5. Janey has a pet crow and learns _____.

You have read stories about small creatures. Is there a small creature you would like to have as a pet? Finish this sentence about a small creature. Write it on your list.

I want a _____ as a pet. I want it because _____.

Writing How-to Directions

You have read stories about small creatures. You have read about their small homes. You have thought about a small creature that you would like to have as a pet. Now you will write how-to directions telling how to make something for that pet. *A Stop Sign for Birds* on page 224 is an example of how-to directions. Follow these steps to write your directions.

Planning

Decide what you want to write your how-to directions about. Make a list of things you will need. Think about the steps. Here is Kate's list of things she will need.

<u>My Notes</u>
<u>Things I Need</u>
   paper towel rolls
   bathroom tissue rolls
   scissors
   hamster food
   hamster

Writing

Use the notes you wrote and the list of steps below to help you.

1. Write your how-to directions.

2. Be sure to write them in the order in which they have to be done.

3. Write a title that tells what the directions are about.

Here are Kate's how-to directions.

How to Make a Hamster Toy

1. First, get a paper towel roll, two bathroom tissue rolls, and scissors.

2. Then, cut two holes in the towel roll.

3. Now, put the other rolls through the holes.

4. Next, put food at the end of the rolls.

5. Last, let the hamster run through the rolls and find the food.

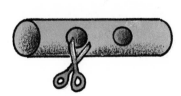 

Checking

Kate trades directions with a friend. Then they ask these questions.

- Can my friend think of any changes I should make?
- Did I write a title for my directions?
- Did I write my directions step by step?
- Did I begin each sentence with a capital letter?
- Did I use end marks at the end of each sentence?

Sharing Your How-to Directions

After you have finished checking your work, you may want to share it with others. Here are two ways to share your how-to directions.

- Make a poster of your own directions. Use pictures to help make them clear.
- Read your directions into a tape recorder. See if another friend can follow them.

This handbook can help you when you write. It tells about marks to use when you change your writing. It tells rules to help you write sentences and use words correctly, and rules to help you use capital letters and punctuation marks. You will also find a model that will help you when you write directions for how to do something.

Use these marks when you make changes in your writing.

Marks	Examples
∧ add	The ⟨little⟩ dog is mine.
ℛ take out	That dog is big and large.
◯ spelling	My ⟨dawg⟩ is the best.

Grammar

On the next four pages, you will find grammar rules and mechanics rules. The rule is on the left in the boxes. To the right, you will find an example of each rule.

Sentences

The rules below tell you about the different kinds of sentences.

Rules	Examples
A **sentence** is a group of words that tells a complete thought. All sentences begin with capital letters.	**J**ohn is tall. **M**y friend is here! **W**hat do you like to do?
A **statement** is a sentence that tells something. A statement ends with a period.	She likes to swim**.**
A **question** is a sentence that asks something. A question ends with a question mark.	Do you like to swim**?**

Grammar

Nouns

The rules below tell you about nouns and how to make nouns name more than one.

Rules	Examples	
A word that names a person, a place, a thing, or an animal is called a **noun**.	girl lake box dog	
Add **s** to most nouns to name more than one.	one cat	three cat**s**
Add **es** to nouns that end in **x**, **ch**, **sh**, or **s** to name more than one.	two box**es** three peach**es** four brush**es** two kiss**es**	
Some nouns change their spelling to name more than one.	one mouse one tooth one child	three mice two teeth two children

Grammar

Verbs

The rules below tell you about verbs.

Rules	Examples
An **action verb** tells what someone or something does.	The children **walk** to school.
Add **s** to an action verb that tells about what one person, animal, or thing does now.	Lee **jumps** over the log.
Add **ed** to a verb to show that the action was in the past.	She **worked** last week.

Mechanics

Capital Letters and Punctuation

These rules will help you make sure you use capital letters and punctuation marks correctly.

Rules	Examples
Begin the name of a person or a pet with a capital letter.	**M**ark **S**mith **S**pot
Begin the names of special places with capital letters.	**S**an **F**rancisco **Y**ellowstone **P**ark **M**aple **S**treet **V**ermont
Begin a title with a capital letter. Use a period after: **D**r., **M**rs., **M**r., and **M**s. Do not use a period after: **M**iss	**D**r. Nancy Suarez **M**r. James Wong **M**iss Ellen Green
The name of each day of the week begins with a capital letter.	**M**onday **W**ednesday
The name of each month and holiday begins with a capital letter.	**T**hanksgiving **J**uly

Models

Writing How-to Directions

Use the model below to help you when you write how-to directions.

How to Make a Bird Feeder

1. First, get a paper plate, string, scissors, and a hole puncher.

2. Next, punch holes in the plate.

3. Now, put the strings in the holes. Tie the strings.

4. Then, put bird seeds on the bird feeder.

5. Last, hang it on a tree.

Note the clue words: *first, next, now, then,* and *last*.

This glossary can help you find the meaning of some of the words in this book. Use it when you are having problems with a word. The directions below will help you understand how the glossary works.

The mark · breaks up the words so you can sound them out, as in the word that follows: **dif·fer·ent**.

Here is how a glossary entry looks:

> **dif·fer·ent** not the same. *We went to three different movies this week.*

A a

acrobat

a·ble knowing how to do something; having the means. *He was able to build a house.*

ac·ro·bat someone who can do flips. *The acrobat did a difficult flip on the mat.*

a·cross from one side to the other. *We watched the glider float across the sky.*

air·plane a flying machine. *I flew in an airplane last year.* **airplanes**

a·long together with someone or something. *I took my dog along on the trip.*

al·read·y by this time. *You are already late.*

an·gry mad. *I got angry when the dog chewed on my coat.*

an·swer to say back to something asked. *She asked me something, and I answered her.* **answers, answered, answering**

an·y at all. *Has my singing gotten any better?*

a·part in pieces. *She took the clock apart after it stopped.*

as·tro·naut one of the crew of a spaceship. *The astronaut blasted off into space.* **astronauts**

angry

apart

B b

base·ball a game played with a bat and ball. *We played baseball all day.*

be·came came to be. *It became too late to see the movie.*

be·gan started. *The race began.*

be·lieve to think something is true. *I believe that our team is the best in town.* **believes, believed, believing**

be·side by the side of; near. *The grass grew beside the fence.*

birth·day the day on which someone was born. *My birthday is on May 4.*

bone

bone a hard piece of the body. *My dog likes chewing on bones.* **bones**

boss·y enjoying to tell others what to do. *I have a very bossy pet.*

bright giving much light. *He rides a bright red bike.*

build to make. *I helped build the new clubhouse.*

bulb the round underground part from which some plants grow. *Dad planted the bulbs in the garden.* **bulbs**

bulb

bunch a set of things of the same kind. *She gave me a bunch of leaves.* **bunches**

bur·y to sink deep in the ground. *The treasure was buried under the tree.* **buries, buried, burying**

C c

circus

can tin jar. *We opened two cans of soup.* **cans**

cir·cus a traveling show of acrobats, clowns, and animals. *We saw an elephant at the circus.*

cit·ies places where many people live. *Most people live in cities.*

claw one of the sharp nails on a bird's or animal's foot. *The kitten's claws are sharp.* **claws**

claw

com·plain to say that something is wrong. *She wanted to complain about the food.* **complains, complained, complaining**

cop·y a thing made to be like another thing. *The teacher handed out copies of the story.* **copies**

cor·ner the place where two lines meet. *The dog chased the cat around the corner.* **corners**

creak to make a sharp noise. *The old chair creaked when Dad sat down.* **creaks, creaked, creaking**

crea·ture any living animal. *The creature lived in the forest.* **creatures**

curb the raised stone along the edge of the sidewalk. *My father parked his car close to the curb.*

D d

dan·ger a chance of harm. *There was no danger of the ship sinking.*

de·cide to make up one's mind. *She has decided to be a dentist when she grows up.* **decides, decided, deciding**

del·i·cate easy to hurt. *The glass lamp is delicate.*

desk

desk a flat place on which to write or read. *I have a new desk at school.* **desks**

die to no longer live. *The plants died because I forgot to water them.* **dies, died, dying**

dome a large rounded roof. *There's a dome over the tennis court.* **domes**

dream something thought while sleeping. *I had a dream last night.* **dreams**

drew made a picture with a pen. *I drew a picture of a funny face.*

dry to empty of water. *The pond dried up in the summer.* **dries, dried, drying**

dust speck of dirt. *The old books were covered with dust.*

E e

earth·quake a shaking of the ground. *The earthquake was scary.* **earthquakes**

ei·ther also. *Then I noticed that the cat had no water, either.*

e·nough as much or as many as needed. *Has he had enough to eat?*

e·ven yet. *You can run even faster if you try.*

F f

faint quiet, weak. *We heard a faint cry.*

fear a feeling of danger. *She has a fear of high places.* **fears**

fence a railing around a yard. *We climbed over the fence.* **fences**

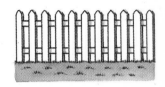

fence

field land with few trees. *We played baseball on the nearby field.* **fields**

fin·ger parts of a hand. *I put the ring on my finger.* **fingers**

flight a trip in an aircraft. *We're going on a flight into space.* **flights**

fuss getting upset. *He made such a fuss when his bike broke.*

G g

gas a liquid that is put in a car. *She filled the tank with gas.*

ger·bil an animal like a mouse. *We keep the gerbils in a cage.* **gerbils**

gerbil

glass something to drink from. *He drank from the glass.* **glasses**

glass·es lenses to help one see better. *She got new glasses.*

glasses

273

greed·y wanting too much. *He was greedy for gold.*

H h

hap·pen to take place. *The storm is about to happen.* **happens, happened, happening**

heard listened. *He heard her calling.*

held gripped. *He held the bat.*

her·o someone who is brave. *The hero saved the puppy.* **heroes**

I i

I'll I will. *I'll clean my room tomorrow.*

im·pos·si·ble not able to be. *It's impossible to be in two places at one time.*

in·ven·tion a making of something new. *The steam engine was a great invention.* **inventions**

it's it is. *It's a new game.*

J j

jacket

jack·et a coat. *She wears a jacket when it's cold.* **jackets**

jade a hard green stone. *Her Dad gave her a jade ring.*

K k

kept held back. *A bad cold kept Kathy from playing in the game.*

kind·ness doing good. *She was known for her kindness.*

knew had the facts. *I knew the answer.*

knock to hit with the fist. *She knocked on the door.* **knocks, knocked, knocking**

knock

L l

large big. *An elephant is a large animal.* **larger, largest**

leak a hole that lets water in. *There's a leak in the roof.* **leaks**

leap to jump. *The cat leaps down from the tree.* **leaps, leaped, leaping**

lip the outside of the mouth. *She wet her lip.* **lips**

lis·ten to try to hear. *I like to listen to songs.* **listens, listened, listening**

M m

ma·chine something that does a job. *We have a new washing machine.* **machines**

main biggest. *The star had the main part in the movie.*

mark a spot made by something. *His feet left marks in the fresh snow.* **marks**

mat·ter to mean something. *Nothing seems to matter when you're sick.* **matters, mattered**

mayor

may·or the head of a city or town. *The mayor walked at the head of the parade.* **mayors**

meant had in mind. *I meant to tell you, but I forgot.*

meat animal flesh. *Dad cooked meat and potatoes.*

mice

mice more than one mouse. *I saw two mice.*

might·y strong and great. *The mighty tree grew from a small seed.*

mild soft and quiet. *A mild breeze blew through the trees.*

milk to get milk from a cow. *The boy milks the cow every morning.* **milks, milked, milking**

mu·se·um place where art or science is shown. *We saw many paintings at the museum.* **museums**

N n

neigh·bor someone who lives nearby. *I helped my neighbor rake his leaves.* **neighbors**

news·pa·per a paper that is printed every day and has news stories. *I bought a newspaper at the store.* **newspapers**

newspaper

nib·ble to take small, quick bites. *The mouse liked to nibble on cheese.* **nibbles, nibbled, nibbling**

note a short bit of writing. *My friend wrote me a note.* **notes**

noth·ing not anything. *I had nothing to do.*

O o

of·ten many times. *We often go to the beach.*

P p

pa·per something used for writing. *I wrote a note on some paper.* **papers**

part a piece, not all. *It snows in this part of the country.* **parts**

par·tic·u·lar special. *I had nothing particular to say to him.*

pay to give in thanks. *I hope this gift will pay you back for all your kindness.* **pays, paid, paying**

piano

per·fect having nothing wrong. *It was perfect weather for a swim.*

per·son man, woman, or child. *There was not a person anywhere.*

pi·an·o something that makes songs. *I'm learning to play the piano.* **pianos**

plan·et a body in space that goes around the sun. *Earth and Mars are planets.* **planets**

play·er one who plays. *She is a good baseball player.* **players**

poem words that sound like a song. *We read a poem about cats.* **poems**

pond a small lake of still water. *There were ducks in the pond.* **ponds**

prob·a·ble likely to happen. *It is not probable that it will snow in the summer.*

prob·lem something to be worked out. *People will need to face many new problems in space.* **problems**

puzzle

puz·zle a game in which pieces make a whole. *I worked on the puzzle.* **puzzles**

Q q

qui·et making little noise. *The class became quiet.*

R r

rack·et a frame with strings. *She hit the ball with the tennis racket.* **rackets**

racket

raise to lift up. *The child raised her hand to answer the teacher.* **raises, raised, raising**

real not made up, true. *Is that your real name?*

real·ly in fact. *The water is really too cold to swim in.*

re·mem·ber to not forget. *I remember everything we did that day.* **remembers, remembered, remembering**

re·port a paper one can write on different ideas. *We read our book reports in class.* **reports**

rug a thick floor covering. *I stepped on the rug.* **rugs**

rug

S s

sail to travel by ship or boat. *We sailed down the river.* **sails, sailed, sailing**

scar·y spooky. *I like scary movies.*

scold to blame. *Mom scolded him for missing dinner.* **scolds, scolded, scolding**

screen a glass layer on which TV is watched. *We have a new TV with a big screen.* **screens**

seen looked at. *I've seen many movies.*

send to cause to be carried. *I am going to send my mother flowers.* **sending**

set went to. *We set to work on painting the house.* **sets, setting**

shin·y bright and smooth. *Her new leather shoes are shiny.*

shiny

shop·keep·er someone who runs a store. *The shopkeeper opened the store in the morning.* **shopkeepers**

side·walk a walkway. *Stay on the sidewalk until the light changes.*

sigh to let out a deep breath. *They started sighing at the end of the sad movie.* **sighs, sighed, sighing**

slice a piece of something. *I had a slice of apple pie.* **slices**

sly tricky. *The sly fox won the race.*

smack to hit, slap. *Our feet smacked the wet street.* **smacks, smacked, smacking**

smile to grin. *She smiled as she gave him the gift.* **smiles, smiled, smiling**

snout the nose, mouth and jaws of an animal. *My dog has a long snout.*

space outside of Earth. *I'd like to go on a trip into space.*

spe·cial one of a kind. *There's a special place where I go to be by myself.*

spent passed time. *I spent the day playing.*

steam what rises from water when it boils. *Steam was coming out of the pot.*

steam

stiff not easily bent. *He had a stiff way of walking.*

street a road in a town or city. *I waited before crossing the street.* **streets**

strength being strong. *She felt that she was running out of strength.*

stretch to draw out. *She stretches her arms when she wakes up.* **stretched, stretching**

such of that kind. *I didn't think that the circus would be such fun.*

sug·gest to come up with an idea. *I suggest we buy a cake for Mom's birthday.* **suggests, suggested, suggesting**

su·per·kid a child who is great. *Ronald Morgan is a superkid!*

swing to move back and forth. *She swings her arms as she walks.* **swinging**

swung moved back and forth. *She swung the baseball bat.*

T t

teach to help to learn. *I want you to teach me how to dance.* **teaches, teaching, taught**

teeth the parts in the mouth used for chewing. *She takes care of her teeth.*

teeth

ten·nis a game. *I liked playing tennis.*

threw tossed. *He threw the ball to me.*

to·mor·row the following day. *Tomorrow we are going to the zoo.*

tongue part of the mouth. *The cat tasted the food with her tongue.* **tongues**

toy something for a child to play with. *I gave my little brother a toy.* **toys**

trans·por·ta·tion the way of going from one place to another. *Transportation is faster and safer than it once was.*

W w

wake to get up from sleep. *She wakes up at seven every day.* **wakes, waked, waking**

warn to give notice of harm. *I came to warn you that a bad storm is heading this way.* **warns, warned, warning**

waste make poor use of. *They wasted their time.* **wastes, wasted, wasting**

watch to look closely. *Watch for cars before you cross.* **watches, watched, watching**

wear to have on. *I forgot to wear my raincoat.* **wears, wearing, wore**

while space of time. *They made us wait a while.*

word speech. *I learned a new word today.* **words**

wor·ry feel uneasy. *Do not worry about me.* **worries, worried, worrying**

wrap to fold something around. *Mother wrapped the scarf around her neck.* **wraps, wrapped, wrapping**

Y y

yard the ground around a house. *I painted the fence around the yard.* **yards**

year 365 days. *Last year I was in first grade.* **years**

yell to cry out. *The boy yelled when he fell down.* **yells, yelled, yelling**

For permission to adapt and reprint copyrighted materials, grateful acknowledgment is made to the following publishers, authors, and other copyright holders. Every effort has been made on the part of the publisher to locate the copyright holders of these materials. Any unintentional omission of acknowledgment for use of these materials will be promptly corrected by the publisher in future reprint editions.

"Afternoon on a Hill" by Edna St. Vincent Millay. From *Collected Poems*, Harper & Row. Copyright © 1917, 1945 by Edna St. Vincent Millay. Reprinted by permission.

"Alexander and the Wind-up Mouse" from *Alexander and the Wind-up Mouse* by Leo Lionni. Copyright © 1969 by Leo Lionni. Used by permission of Pantheon Books, a division of Random House, Inc.

"The Best New Thing," adaptation of "The Best New Thing" by Isaac Asimov. Text copyright © 1971 by Isaac Asimov. Reprinted by permission of Philomel Books.

"Cat" by Mary Britton Miller. Copyright © estate of Mary Britton Miller.

"Cats" from *The Children's Bells* by Eleanor Farjeon. Copyright © 1957 by Eleanor Farjeon. Reprinted by permission of Harold Ober Associates Incorporated.

"Digging Up Dinosaurs" adapted from *Digging Up Dinosaurs* written and illustrated by Aliki. Copyright © 1981 by Aliki Brandenberg. Reprinted by permission of Thomas Y. Crowell, an imprint of Harper & Row, Publishers, Inc.

"Evan's Corner" adapted from *Evan's Corner* by Elizabeth Starr Hill. Copyright © 1961 by Elizabeth Starr Hill. Reprinted by permission of Harold Ober Associates Incorporated.

"Everybody Says" by Dorothy Aldis, reprinted by permission of G. P. Putnam's Sons, from *Here, There and Everywhere* by Dorothy Aldis. Copyright © 1927, 1928; copyright renewed 1955, 1956 by Dorothy Aldis.

"Holding Hands" by Lenore Link. Copyright © by Instructor Publications, Inc. Used by permission.

"Horton Hears a Who" from *Horton Hears a Who* by Dr. Seuss. Copyright © 1954 by Dr. Seuss. Reprinted by permission of Random House, Inc.

"I Have a Sister, My Sister Is Deaf" from *I Have a Sister, My Sister Is Deaf* written by Jeanne Whitehouse Peterson, illustrated by Deborah Kay. Text copyright © 1977 by Jeanne Whitehouse Peterson. Illustrations copyright © 1977 by Deborah Ray. Reprinted by permission of Harper & Row, Publishers, Inc.

"I Like Bugs" by Margaret Wise Brown from *The Friendly Book*. Copyright © 1954 by Western Publishing Company, Inc. Used by permission.

"In My Treehouse" excerpted portions from *In My Treehouse* by Alice Schertle. Copyright © 1983 by Alice Schertle. Used by permission of Lothrop, Lee & Shepard Books (a Division of William Morrow & Company).

"Janey's Boss" from *The Magic Spectacles and Other Easy-To-Read Stories* by Lilian Moore. Copyright © 1965 by Lilian Moore. Reprinted by permission of Bantam Books. All rights reserved.

"Jenny and the Tennis Nut" from *Jenny and the Tennis Nut* by Janet Schulman. Copyright © 1978 by Janet Schulman. Adapted by permission of Greenwillow Books (A Division of William Morrow & Company).

"Little Gorilla" from *Little Gorilla* by Ruth Bornstein. Copyright © 1976 by Ruth Bornstein. Reprinted by permission of Clarion Books/Ticknor & Fields, a Houghton Mifflin Company.

"Little Talk" by Aileen Fisher, from *Up the Windy Hill*, published by Abelard-Shuman, New York. Copyright © 1953 by Aileen Fisher. Copyright renewed 1981. By permission of the author.

"Max" written and illustrated by Rachel Isadora. *Max* by Rachel Isadora is reprinted by permission of Macmillan Publishing Company. Copyright © 1976 Rachel Isadora.

"Mice" from *Fifty-One New Nursery Rhymes* by Rose Fyleman. Copyright © 1932 by Doubleday, a division of Bantam, Doubleday, Dell Publishing Group, Inc. Reprinted by permission of the publisher and the Society of Authors as the literary representative of the Estate of Rose Fyleman.

"No Time for Tina" from *No Time for Tim* by Bonnie Knight. Copyright © 1983 by Bonnie Knight. Used by permission of the author.

"The Old Woman" from *You Know the old woman* (8 lines) and one illustration from *Appley Dapply's Nursery Rhymes* by Beatrix Potter (Frederick Warne & Co., 1917), copyright © Frederick Warne & Co., 1917.

"Picture People" from *Whispers and Other Poems* by Myra Cohn Livingston. Copyright © 1958 by Myra Cohn Livingston. Reprinted by permission of Marian Reiner for the author.

"The Rice Bowl Pet" by Patricia Miles Martin. Copyright © 1962 by Patricia Miles Martin. Reprinted by permission of Patrick J. Gallagher, Executor.

"Snail" by Langston Hughes from *Selected Poems of Langston Hughes*. Copyright © 1926 by Alfred A. Knopf, Inc. and renewed 1954 by Langston Hughes. Reprinted by permission of Alfred A. Knopf, Inc.

"This is My Rock" from *One at a Time* by David McCord. Copyright © 1929 by David McCord. First appeared in *Saturday Review*. By permission of Little, Brown & Co., Inc.

"Veronica" adapted by permission of Alfred A. Knopf, Inc. from *Veronica* by Roger Duvoisin. Copyright © 1961 by Roger Duvoisin.

"Watch Out, Ronald Morgan!" from *Watch Out, Ronald Morgan!* written by Patricia Reilly Giff. Text copyright © 1985 by Patricia Reilly Giff. Used by permission of Viking Penguin Inc.

"The Whales Off Wales" from *One Winter Night in August and Other Nonsense Jingles* by X. J. Kennedy. Copyright © 1975 by X. J. Kennedy. Reprinted by permission of Curtis Brown, Ltd.

"What Is That Alligator Saying?" from *What Is That Alligator Saying?* by Ruth Belov Gross. Copyright © 1972. Reprinted by permission of Scholastic Inc.

Illustration

Yvette Banek, 38-40, 42-44; Ruth Bornstein, 145-146; Aliki Brandenberg, 156-164; Randy Chewning, 78-80; Kitty Diamantis, 9, 202-203; Ivan Dieruf, 224; Roger Duvoisin, 184, 187-193, 195; Elizabeth Fong, 210-211, 213-214; Friso Henstra, 230-236; Dennis Hockerman, 90-98; Rachel Isadora, 16-17, 18; Kristine Juzaitis, 268-283; Leo Lionni, 238-253; Rosanne Litzinger, 8, 10-11, 19, 37, 81, 103, 139, 140-141, 147, 209; Laura Lydecker, 100-101; Diana Magnuson, 118-120, 123, 125-128, 130-131; Benton Mahan, 20-24; Leslie Morrill, 148-154; Stan Tusan, 46-54; Trinka Noble, 82-83, 85-88; John O'Brien, 36; Betty Frank Plumlee, 102; Beatrix Potter, 236; Jan Pyk, 166; Deborah Kogan Ray, 57, 59, 60-61, 63, 65, 66, 67; Vera Rosenberry, 168, 170-172, 216-219, 221-222; Claudia Karabaic Sargent, 7, 74-75; Karen Schmidt, 174, 176-182; Dr. Seuss, 206-208; Jerry Smath, 110-116; Kirsten Soderlind, 6, 12-13; Ashley Wolff, 226-228.

Photography

David Kammer 68; Culver Pictures, Inc. 105; The Granger Collection 106; Tim Holt/Photo Researchers 107; Omni-Photo Communications 108; The Bronxville Studio 132; J.C. Carton/Bruce Coleman, Inc. 149; Bruce Coleman, Inc. 150; E.R. Degginger/Animals, Animals 151; Ted Levin/Animals, Animals 152; S.J. Kraseman/Peter Arnold, Inc. 153; Courtesy of Little, Brown and Company 198; Courtesy of Random House 254.